THE CHILDREN'S HOUR

Best Loved Poems

A BOOK TO GROW ON

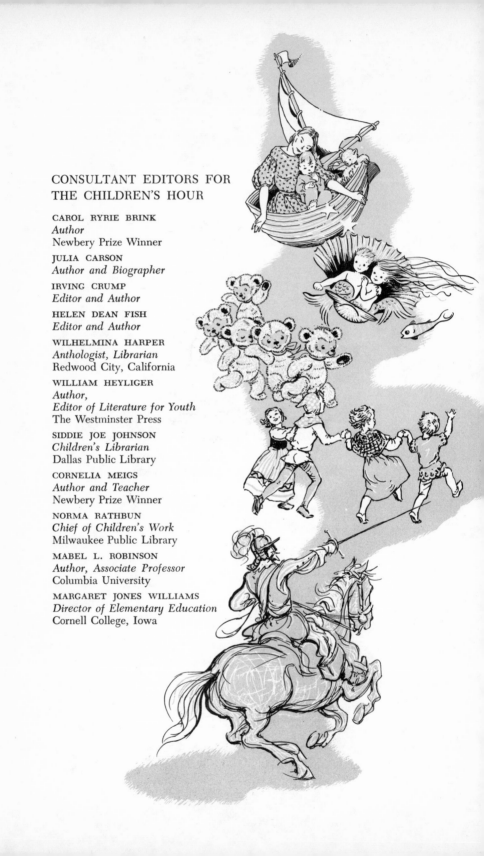

CONSULTANT EDITORS FOR THE CHILDREN'S HOUR

CAROL RYRIE BRINK
Author
Newbery Prize Winner

JULIA CARSON
Author and Biographer

IRVING CRUMP
Editor and Author

HELEN DEAN FISH
Editor and Author

WILHELMINA HARPER
Anthologist, Librarian
Redwood City, California

WILLIAM HEYLIGER
Author,
Editor of Literature for Youth
The Westminster Press

SIDDIE JOE JOHNSON
Children's Librarian
Dallas Public Library

CORNELIA MEIGS
Author and Teacher
Newbery Prize Winner

NORMA RATHBUN
Chief of Children's Work
Milwaukee Public Library

MABEL L. ROBINSON
Author, Associate Professor
Columbia University

MARGARET JONES WILLIAMS
Director of Elementary Education
Cornell College, Iowa

MARJORIE BARROWS, *Editor*

Best Loved Poems

MATHILDA SCHIRMER
Associate Editor

DOROTHY SHORT
Art Editor

THE CHILDREN'S HOUR

PRINTED IN THE UNITED STATES OF AMERICA

Acknowledgments

The editor and publishers wish to thank the following publishers and agents for permission to use and reprint poems and illustrations in this book:

BEN ABRAMSON, ARGUS BOOKS, INC., for "He Whom a Dream Hath Possessed" by Shaemus O'Sheel.

AMERICAN JUNIOR RED CROSS NEWS and the author for "Sniff" and "Easter in the Woods" by Frances Frost.

APPLETON-CENTURY-CROFTS, INC., for "Acorns" from *Fifty Country Rhymes for Children* by E. L. M. King, copyright, 1926, D. Appleton & Company.

MRS. GEORGE BAMBRIDGE for "The Seal's Lullaby" and "Recessional" by Rudyard Kipling.

BASIL BLACKWELL & MOTT, LTD., for "The Apple Rhyme" from *Ring-a-Ring O' Fairies* by Madeleine Nightingale and "The Caravan" from *Nursery Lays of Nursery Days* by Madeleine Nightingale; and "Choosing Shoes" by Ffrida Wolfe.

BRANDT & BRANDT for "Travel" from *Second April* by Edna St. Vincent Millay, published by Harper & Brothers, copyright, 1921, 1949, by Edna St. Vincent Millay; "God's World" from *Renascence and Other Poems* by Edna St. Vincent Millay, published by Harper & Brothers, copyright, 1913, 1941, by Edna St. Vincent Millay.

CURTIS BROWN, LTD., and the author for "Jonathan Bing Dances for Spring," "More about Jonathan Bing," and "A New Song to Sing about Jonathan Bing" from *Jonathan Bing and Other Verses* by Beatrice Curtis Brown, copyright, 1936, by Beatrice Curtis Brown.

CHILDREN'S ACTIVITIES and the author for "Happy Day" by Betty Jump.

THE CHRISTIAN SCIENCE PUBLISHING SOCIETY for "If I Were Otherwise" by Joyce L. Brisley, and "Air Mail" by Gordon Hillman, from *The Christian Science Monitor.*

DODD, MEAD & COMPANY, INC., for "The Cremation of Sam McGee" by Robert Service.

DOUBLEDAY & COMPANY, INC., for "The Animal Store," "The General Store," "I'd Like to Be a Lighthouse," "If Once You Have Slept on an Island," and "The Playhouse Key" from *Taxis and Toadstools* by Rachel Field, copyright, 1926, Doubleday & Company, Inc.; "The Boat" and "If Only" from *Gay Go Up* by Rose Fyleman, copyright, 1929, 1930, by Doubleday & Company, Inc.; "Mrs. Brown," "Mice," "Please," and "Fairy Lore" from *The Fairy Green* by Rose Fyleman, copyright, 1923, by Doubleday & Company, Inc.; "Consolation" from *The Fairy Flute* by Rose Fyleman, copyright, 1923, by Doubleday and Company, Inc.; "Trees" from *Trees and Other Poems* by Joyce Kilmer, copyright, 1914, by Doubleday & Company, Inc.; and "Recessional" from *The Five Nations* by Rudyard Kipling, copyright, 1903, by Rudyard Kipling.

E. P. DUTTON & CO., INC., for "Galoshes" from *Stories to Begin on* by Rhoda W. Bacmeister, published and copyright, 1940, E. P. Dutton & Co., Inc., N. Y.; "The Dinner Horses" from *Here and Now Story Book* by Lucy Sprague Mitchell, published and copyright, 1921, E. P. Dutton & Co., Inc., N. Y., renewed, 1948, Lucy Sprague Mitchell; and "The House of the Mouse" from *Another Here and Now Story Book* edited by Lucy Sprague Mitchell, published and copyright, 1937, E. P. Dutton & Co., Inc., N. Y.

MRS. VIDA L. GUITERMAN for "The Chant of the Chipmunk," "Chums," "The Friendly Pup," and "Pet Show" by Arthur Guiterman.

HARCOURT, BRACE AND COMPANY, INC., for "Small Homes" and "Splinter" from *Good Morning, America* by Carl Sandburg, copyright, 1928, by Carl Sandburg; "The Family Dragon," "The Hollow Tree House," and "The Secret Cavern" from *Little Girl and Boy Land* by Margaret Widdemer, copyright, 1924, by Harcourt, Brace and Company, Inc.

HARPER & BROTHERS for "Christmas in the Woods" from *Christmas in the Woods* by Frances Frost, copyright, 1942, by Frances Frost; "Policemen on Parade" from *Puddin' and Pie* by James Garthwaite, copyright, 1929, Harper & Brothers; "Familiar Friends" from *I Spend the Summer* by James S. Tippett, copyright, 1930, Harper & Brothers; "My Dog" from *I Know Some Little Animals* by James S. Tippett, copyright, 1941, Harper & Brothers; and "Trains" from *I Go A Traveling* by James S. Tippett, copyright, 1929, Harper & Brothers.

The writers themselves obtained permission when necessary to reprint their selections from periodicals in which they first appeared. The compiler joins them in thanking:

American Girl for "Song for a Country Night"; *The Chicago Tribune* for "The Aristocrat," "The Dinosaur," "Ever See a Rhea," "The Fairy Phone," "Field Flowers," "The Hornbill Family," "Octopus," "The Present," "The Puddle," and "A Strange Beast"; *Child Life Magazine* for "Attic Trunk," "The Birthday of Our Land," "Boredom," "The Bunny," "The Camel," "Child's Prayer," "Christmas Song," "Cross-Stitch Sampler," "Discomfort," "Fawn's First Journey," "Field Mouse," "The First Night," "First Thanksgiving of All," "The Flamingo," "Frogs," "Good Morning," "Gratitude," "The Great Craftsman," "Halloween," "Happily Ever After," "Happiness," "Harbor of Hushaby Ho," "Heroism," "I Stare at the Cow," "I Wish I Lived in Elfland," "In Grandmother's Garden," "Lincoln," "Little Girl Next Door," "The Magic Screen," "The Mist and All," "Mud," "The Organ Grinder's Garden," "Our Street," "Packages," "Paths," "The Pirate," "Planting a Tree," "The Rain Toys," "Round the Maypole Now We Dance," "Self-Control," "Sing, World, Sing," "Song at Dusk," "Spring Signs," "Stephen Wants a Mouse," "Tamed," "Tidy Turtle," "Tim," "Valentine to My Doll," "Washington," "Why the Winds Blow," "Wind," and "Wishes"; *The Christian Science Monitor* for "Cool," "Indian Boy," "Indian Song," "The Lady Slipper," and "New Snow"; *Good Housekeeping* for "Song of Gray Things"; *Jack and Jill* for "Bedtime Story," "Child's Prayer for Other Children," "First Snowfall," "Forest Lullaby," "The Garden Hat Shop," "Goblin Gadgets," "The Home-Made Ship," "Little Woodchuck's Fright," and "Seashore Gossip"; *Ladies' Home Journal* for "Cradle Song"; *Our Dumb Animals* for "The Christmas Calf," "Shares," "Song of the Herd," "Spring Pasture," and "Thanksgiving"; *Story Parade* for "Deep Sea Adventure," "The Frog," "Remembering the Winter," "The Second-Hand Shop," "The Witch of Willowby Wood," and "Witch Cat"; and *Westways* for "Summer."

We also thank the following authors for permission to reprint various poems of theirs:

Marjorie Allen Anderson, Mildred Leigh Anderson, Mildred Bowers Armstrong, Faith Baldwin, Janet Norris Bangs, Marjorie Barrows, Mary Beimfohr, Rowena Bennett, Bee Bowers, Berton Braley, Fannie R. Buchanan, Polly Chase, Marchette Chute, Fleur Conkling, Ruth Crary, Jeanne De Lamarter, Ruth Dixon, Glenn Ward Dresbach, Ivy O. Eastwick, Clara Edmonds-Hemingway, Aileen Fisher, Carolyn Forsyth, Elsie Melchert Fowler, Frances Frost, Eugene Garnett for poem by Louise Garnett, Etta F. Gilbert, Marguerite Gode, Vivian G. Gouled, Frances Barbara Grafe, Scharmel Iris, Bertha Ten Eyck James, Florence Page Jaques, Eleanor Jewett, Emilie Fendall Johnson, Siddie Joe Johnson, Clare Joslyn, Betty Jump, Carl S. Junge, Maurice Lesemann, Elizabeth-Ellen Long, Adelaide Love, Lawrence McKinney, Lorena La Brec Ouellette, Josephine Van Dolzen Pease, Anne Pérez-Guerra, Ruth Stephens Porter, Clara E. Randall, Laura Lee Randall, Mary Louise Scott, Marion K. Seavey, Johnny Sloan, Fredrika Shumway Smith, Louise de Marigny Smith, Leona Stafford, Eleanor Elizabeth Stevens, Gertrude Strickler, Marion Strobel, Adele Jordan Tarr, Nancy Byrd Turner, Maud E. Uschold, Judy Van der Veer, J. Lilian Vandevere, Caroline P. Wild, Caroline S. P. Wild, Dixie Willson, Helen Wing, Edith Franklin Wyatt, Ella Young, and Ann Zelenka.

We also thank the following artists for various illustrations of theirs:

Juanita Bennett, Clarence Biers, Rosemary Buehrig, Marchette Chute, Pelagie Doane, Frances Eckart, Barbara Fitzgerald, Esther Friend, John Gee, Denise Giraud, Paul Hamlin, Frances Tipton Hunter, Elizabeth Orton Jones, Dorothy Lathrop, Robert Lawson, Mahrea Cramer Lehman, Joan Leitz, John Dukes McKee, John Merryweather, Decie Merwin, Maud and Miska Petersham, Eveline Rader, Walter R. Sabel, Robert Sinnott, Susan Snider, Anne Stossel, Margaret W. Tarrant, Christine Tavridis, Diana Thorne, Beverly Treybal, Ruth Van Telligen, and Keith Ward.

Contents

Part I: EVERYDAY POEMS

GOOD MORNING
Fannie R. Buchanan

Good morning, sky!
Good morning, sun!
Good morning, little winds that run!
Good morning, birds!
Good morning, trees,
And creeping grass, and brownie bees!
How did you find out it was day?
Who told you night had gone away?
I'm wide awake;
I'm up now, too.
I'll be right out to play with you!

GRANDMOTHER'S BROOK
Rachel Field

Grandmother tells me about a brook
   She used to pass on her way to school;
A quick, brown brook with a rushing sound,
   And moss green edges, thick and cool.
When she was the age that I am now
   She would cross over it, stone by stone,
I like to think how she must have looked
   Under the greenery, all alone.
Sometimes I ask her:—"Is it there,
   That brook you played by,—the same, today?"
And she says she hasn't a doubt it is—
   It's children who change and go away.

OVER THE GARDEN WALL*
Eleanor Farjeon

Over the garden wall,
Where unseen children play,
Somebody threw a ball
One fine summer day.
I caught it as it came
Straight from the hand unknown
Playing a happy game
It would not play alone.

A pretty ball with bands
Of gold and stars of blue;
I turned it in my hands
And wondered, then I threw
Over the garden wall
Again the treasure round—
And somebody caught the ball
With a laughing sound.

*Reprinted by permission of the publishers, J. B. Lippincott Company, from *Eleanor Farjeon's Poems for Children.*
Copyright, 1951, by Eleanor Farjeon.

HAPPINESS

Jeanne De Lamarter

Oh, Mother, don't you love the wind?
It circles round the hill.
It makes my hair stand up on end,
And makes my breath stand still!

Oh, Mother, don't you love the wind?
It whistles flying by.
It makes umbrellas of my dress,
And tumbles up the sky!

WORLD SECRETS

Marjorie H. Hayes

Pebbles on the sandy beach
Are older, far, than I;
Washed from shore to shore, they've seen
Centuries roll by.

Cave men probably admired
These pebbles flecked with gold,
And those, perhaps, were skipping stones
For pirates fierce and bold.

The roaring of the dinosaurs
Around the world they heard;
And yet they lie all unconcerned,
And will not say a word.

3

SANDPILE TOWN
Aileen Fisher

It took at least a morning
of working in the sun
and even then our village
was just a sandpile one—
the roads beyond the suburbs
were only just begun,
the little lakes we put in
were only just-for-fun—
how long it must have taken,
how LONG it must have taken,
how long it must have TAKEN
before the World got done!

A HILLY LITTLE TOWN
Aileen Fisher

On the side of a hill in a very hilly land
I built a hilly village of pine cones and sand,
I made a lovely mansion with green moss towers
And in the mansion garden I put lichen flowers.

A little white road wandered past the doors
Of the shopkeepers' homes to the shopkeepers' stores,
And on past the church was the village square
With a shell for a fountain and a chip for a chair.

Twigs were the trees in my hilly little town,
And fireflies were lights when the sun went down.

BEING A GYPSY
Barbara Young

A gypsy, a gypsy,
Is what I'd like to be,
If ever I could find one who
Would change his place with me.
Rings on my fingers,
Earrings in my ears,
Rough shoes to roam the world
For years and years and years!
I'd listen to the stars,
I'd listen to the dawn,
I'd learn the tunes of wind and rain,
The talk of fox and faun.
A gypsy, a gypsy!
To ramble and to roam
For maybe—oh,
A week or so—
And then I'd hie me home!

THE OLD COUNTRY
Ann Zelenka

Sometimes when you tell me . . .
I remember years before
When we lived in a house
With a sky blue door.
The table was bumpy
And all over slivers,
And out of the window
Were hills and rivers,
There were stones in the river
And caves in the hill,
And gypsies camped
By the flour mill.
The tulips were yellow,
The rabbits were tame;
The trees were all tall
And they whispered my name.

5

THE NIGHTINGALE
Ivy O. Eastwick

The Nightingale
made up a tune
about the foxgloves
and the moon.

She sang it high,
she sang it low!
it was as dreamful
and as slow
as summer moonlight
on the lea . . .

she sang it three times
round to me.

THE STAR

Marjorie Barrows

And when the night climbs up our hill
And all the world is very still,
A little star away up high
Is staring at me from the sky.

It hangs alone up in the air
And when I see it shining there
A something in me sort of sings
And then I always wonder things.

I wonder how it likes to see
A far-off little girl like me,
And how the world looks up so far
And how it *feels* to be a star!

6

Pelagie Doane

THE FAMILY DRAGON
Margaret Widdemer

Last night there walked across our lawn a beast we didn't know—
We saw his little footprints marked quite plainly in the snow.

It might have been an ocelot, or perhaps a grizzly bear—
We *hoped* it was a dragon, come out walking from its lair;

We didn't want a grown-up one, all fire and scales and foam,
But just a baby dragonlet that we could carry home;

We'd keep him in the nursery and give him a nice name,
And have him for a family pet, with ribbons on, quite tame.

We tracked him down the meadow path and all along the hedge
And there his little footprints stopped close up beneath the edge,

For there the snow had gone away—there wasn't any track—
And it was teatime anyway, so both of us went back.

But we shall go some day quite soon and find him in his lair,
And capture him while he's asleep, and tie him up with care,

And we will have the 'spressman come and put him in his wagon
And bring him home to stay with us and be our family dragon!

7

ROLLING DOWN A HILL

Dorothy Aldis

Rolling
Down a
Hill my
Head
Turns in-
To my
Feet in-
Stead;

And the
Grass tops
And the
Sky
Tangle up
Up as
I go
By.

Cows and
Trees are
Tumbled
Till
I reach the
Bottom
Of the
Hill.

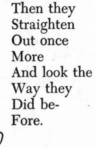

Then they
Straighten
Out once
More
And look the
Way they
Did be-
Fore.

My feet are
Where they
Used to
Be—
My head is back on top of me.

8

WHAT I WOULD DO

Dorothy Aldis

I *wish* she'd give away my plate
For I know how I'd rather eat:
Off of a stone—
A nice and flat and
Smooth white stone.
I'd eat off that
And drink from harebells.
I'm sure twenty
Filled with milk
Would be plenty.

I *wish* she'd give away my bed.
I'd love it if my mother said:
"Today I gave away your bed."
For I know where I'd sleep:

Up in the hay
Where it's nice and warm and
Twice last year
Some kittens were born and
That's where I'd sleep
In the sweet and musty
Hay and get
My hair all dusty.

TREE–CHILDREN

Mary Carolyn Davies

The little trees that to the breeze
Make quaint and timorous courtesies:
I like to come and play with these.

Each grown-up pine that stands in line
Is but a stranger great and fine—
The *little* trees are friends of mine!

9

THE CAVE

Glenn Ward Dresbach

They had found the cave a year ago
After some rocks had slid to show
The opening, and they could see
The cave was big enough to be
Just right for all they had in mind.
When they crawled in they were pleased to find
The floor of stone was clean and dry,
The walls were firm and the roof was high—
So they could build a fire and sit
To watch the dreams that danced in it,
Away from wind and rain or chill . . .
They went home excited, over the hill.
But one day, when they came once more,
They saw, asleep in sun at the door,
Three little raccoons like fuzzy balls
That awakened and rolled inside the walls—
And then peeked out with shining eyes
To see what had taken them by surprise . . .
So they decided, then and there,
That it would not be right to scare
The little raccoons from the cave. With pride,
They knew they could think of them inside,
Safe and warm—for the cave was too small
For grown-up hunters who wished to crawl
Inside . . . and the heart big enough to hold
Something the hunters must not be told!

THE WOODPECKER

Elizabeth Madox Roberts

The woodpecker pecked out a little round hole
And made him a house in the telephone pole.
One day when I watched he poked out his head,
And he had on a hood and a collar of red.
When the streams of rain pour out of the sky,
And the sparkles of lightning go flashing by,
And the big, big wheels of thunder roll,
He can snuggle back in the telephone pole.

10

THE BUTTERBEAN TENT
Elizabeth Madox Roberts

All through the garden I went and went,
And I walked in under the butterbean tent.

The poles leaned up like a good tepee
And made a nice little house for me.

I had a hard brown clod for a seat,
And all outside was a cool green street.

A little green worm and a butterfly
And a cricket-like thing that could hop went by.

Hidden away there were flocks and flocks
Of bugs that could go like little clocks.

Such a good day it was when I spent
A long, long while in the butterbean tent.

PRINCIPAL EXPORTS
Marchette Chute

In China they wear pigtails,
As pirates used to do.
In Asia they have elephants,
And in the Congo, too.

In Holland they have windmills,
In Ceylon they grow tea,
And in the South Sea Islands
There is a breadfruit tree.

In England there are rabbits,
In Greenland they make lard.
In Java there are turtles;
Geography isn't hard.

THE FINGER CHURCH
Eleanor Jewett

My mother has the strangest hands—
They make a church; they make a steeple—
And when the front doors open wide
They make just half a dozen people!

The steeple rises tall as tall,
Her thumbs make stately, massive doors—
And then she laughs and turns her hands
And out the stream of people pours!

12

LITTLE

Dorothy Aldis

I am the sister of him
And he is my brother.
He is too little for us
To talk to each other.

So every morning I show him
My doll and my book;
But every morning he still is
Too little to look.

THE BABY

Marchette Chute

I like our baby well enough
  When she isn't underfoot,
But she will go crawling all around
  No matter where she's put.

And yesterday she sat square down
  On a place she shouldn't sit
And smashed my new electric train;
  I'll be weeks at fixing it.

And when I went to pick her up,
  She gave a little purr
And rubbed her nose against my cheek;
  I'm kind of fond of her.

SPRING RAIN

Marchette Chute

The storm came up so very quick
    It couldn't have been quicker.
I should have brought my hat along,
    I should have brought my slicker.

My hair is wet, my feet are wet,
    I couldn't be much wetter.
I fell into a river once,
    But this is even better.

MUD

Polly Chase

Mud is very nice to feel
All squishy-squash between the toes!
I'd rather wade in wiggly mud
Than smell a yellow rose.

Nobody else but the rosebush knows
How nice mud feels
Between the toes.

GALOSHES*

Rhoda W. Bacmeister

Susie's galoshes
Make splishes and sploshes
And slooshes and sloshes,
As Susie steps slowly
Along in the slush.

They stamp and they tramp
On the ice and concrete,
They get stuck in the muck and the mud;
But Susie likes much better to hear

The slippery slush
As it slooshes and sloshes,
And splishes and sploshes,
All round her galoshes!

*Taken from *Stories To Begin On*, by Rhoda W. Bacmeister, published and copyright, 1940, by E. P. Dutton & Co., Inc., New York.

14

FARMERS

Marchette Chute

Farmers have horses,
And cows,
And ducks,
And always a hen
That sits and clucks,

And sometimes
A little
Baby pig.
So we're being farmers
When we
Grow
Big.

MY PLAN

Marchette Chute

When I'm a little older
 I plan to buy a boat,
And up and down the river
 The two of us will float.

I'll have a little cabin
 All painted white and red
With shutters for the window
 And curtains for the bed.

I'll have a little cookstove
 On which to fry my fishes,
And all the Hudson River
 In which to wash my dishes.

15

IRONING
Dorothy Aldis

The smell of ironing being done
Is very pleasant to the nose—
It's not like flowers in the sun
Or new-baked cookies laid in rows,
But just as fresh and warm a whiff
Rises on any ironing day
From little dresses, starched and stiff,
Waiting to go out and play.

LOOKING IN
Dorothy Aldis

Coming home one winter's night
Passing windows warm and bright,
We looked through and we could see
People snug as they could be.

Safe inside, they didn't know
That it was cold out in the snow,
Or how it prickled on my chin,
Or how I stood there looking in.

EXPLORER
Polly Chase

Although the sun has almost set
My brother hasn't come home yet.

Before he went he patted the cat
And put Mercurochrome on a scratch.
Then he took his pirate patch
And boy scout knife and cowboy hat
Out of the bottom bureau drawer.

He *said* he was going to Labrador.

16

THE SECRET PLACE
Dorothy Aldis

Half way up a certain tree
There's a place belongs to me.
Two branches make a little chair
And I like it setting there.

I like it.
And it's secret too.
No grownup guesses where I go.
And if he should, and climbed to it—
He would not fit, he would not fit!

THE CLOWN
Dorothy Aldis

I like to see
The spotted clown.
He throws dishes
In the air,
And when they've started
Coming down
Looks as though
He didn't care,
But catches each one
Perfectly
Over and over
Every time:
One and two and
One-two-three,
Like a pattern,
Or a rhyme.

17

CHOOSING SHOES
Ffrida Wolfe

New shoes, new shoes,
Red and pink and blue shoes,
Tell me, what would *you* choose
If they'd let us buy?

Buckle shoes, bow shoes,
Pretty pointy-toe shoes,
Strappy, cappy low shoes;
Let's have some to try.

Bright shoes, white shoes,
Dandy dance-by-night shoes,
Perhaps-a-little-tight shoes;
Like some? So would I.

BUT

Flat shoes, fat shoes,
Stump-along-like-that shoes,
Wipe-them-on-the-mat shoes,
O that's the sort they'll buy.

PACKAGES
Adelaide Love

Isn't it fun to open packages?
Isn't it fun to guess
What's in them first? It might be a doll
Or a game or a party dress.

I like them best when they come with ribbons
And bows to be untied,
And pretty seals that you have to tear
Before you can look inside.

THE PRESENT

Eleanor Jewett

My Aunt Frances gave me a sweater,
  Red like a rose with a duck in the middle;
When I'm dressed up I wear my sweater
  And my breather makes the duck go jaggledy-jiddle.

Jaggledy-jiddle goes my white duck,
  And I breathe my stomach way out to see
If he flops his wings, but he never does,
  He just stares quietly back at me.

My white duck has a yellow foot
  And a yellow bill and he sleeps in a drawer.
When I undress he goes straight to sleep
  And sleeps till I get him and breathe some more.

MY FRIEND LU

Ruth Dixon

I lunch each day with my friend Lu,
Who wears his hair in a long black queue.
He smiles at me and is never late,
For he lives on my Chinese plate!

19

SNOW BY NIGHT

Rachel Field

Snow is falling tonight,
  The tallest buildings seem
Angular phantoms dim
  As the texture of a dream.
Snow at the windowpane,
  And we who watch it blow,
Slanting and fine and white,
  Must whisper, "Even so
It fell on roofs of old,
  On streets of long ago,
On the watchman calling, 'Twelve
  O' the clock, and a fall of snow!'"

CIRCUS*

Eleanor Farjeon

The brass band blares,
The naphtha flares,
The sawdust smells,
Showmen ring bells,
And oh! right into the circus-ring
Comes such a lovely, lovely thing,
A milk-white pony with flying tress,
And a beautiful lady,
A beautiful lady,
A *beautiful* lady in a pink dress!
The red-and-white clown
For joy tumbles down.
Like a pink rose
Round she goes
On her tiptoes
With the pony under—
And then, oh, wonder!
The pony his milk-white tresses droops,
And the beautiful lady,
The *beautiful* lady,
Flies like a bird through the paper hoops!
The red-and-white clown for joy falls dead,
Then he waggles his feet and stands on his head,
And the little boys on the twopenny seats
Scream with laughter and suck their sweets.

*Reprinted by permission of the publishers, J. B. Lippincott Company, from *Eleanor Farjeon's Poems for Children.*
Copyright, 1951, by Eleanor Farjeon.

THE CIRCUS

Elizabeth Madox Roberts

Friday came and the circus was there,
And Mother said that the twins and I
And Charles and Clarence and all of us
Could go out and see the parade go by.

And there were wagons with pictures on,
And you never could guess what they had inside,
Nobody could guess, for the doors were shut,
And there was a dog that a monkey could ride.

A man on the top of a sort of cart
Was clapping his hands and making a talk.
And the elephant came—he can step pretty far—
It made us laugh to see him walk.

Three beautiful ladies came riding by,
And each one had on a golden dress,
And each one had a golden whip.
They were queens of Sheba, I guess.

A big wild man was in a cage,
And he had some snakes going over his feet.
And somebody said, "He eats them alive!"
But I didn't see him eat.

23

I CAN BE A TIGER

Mildred Leigh Anderson

I can't go walking
When They say no,
And I can't go riding
Unless They go,
I can't splash puddles
In my shiny new shoes,
But I can be a tiger
Whenever I choose.

I can't eat peanuts
And I can't eat cake,
I have to go to bed,
When They stay awake,
I can't bang windows
And I mustn't tease,
But I can be an elephant
As often as I please.

THE SEA HORSE

Fleur Conkling

I went to find a sea horse
One day to take a ride,
I thought I'd climb up on his back
And if he reared or shied,

I'd check up on the reins a bit
And wheel him round about,
Then let him gallop terribly fast
Till "Whoa!" at him I'd shout!

But when I found a sea horse
In rocks quite near the sea,
I held him carefully in my hand—
AND HE RODE HOME ON ME!

IF ONLY . . .

Rose Fyleman

If only I'd some money,
    I'd buy a jolly boat
And get a pair of sea boots
    And a furry sort of coat,
A case or two of salted beef
    And a seaman's wooden chest,
And I'd sail away to the North Pole
Or I'd sail away to the South Pole,
    Whichever I thought was best.

I'd get up very early—
    They wouldn't see me go—
Jimmy would be with me
    But no one else would know.
Dogs are very useful
    And I couldn't part with Jim,
And whether I went to the North Pole,
Or whether I went to the South Pole,
    It would be all the same to him.

THE BOAT

Rose Fyleman

Sleeping in a cabin is as jolly as can be,
And it's fun to throw your rubbish out straight into the sea;
And the captain is so handsome, with gold upon his coat,
And I do like living on a boat.

The steward gives me apples, and orange juice to drink,
And the lamps are lit at lunchtime, all beautiful and pink;
And there's soup with little letters in, and lovely stripy ice
And when the floor went wobbly it was nice.

We haven't seen a mermaid, we haven't had a wreck,
But I've never known a nursery so thrilling as a deck;
I never do a lesson, I never play a note. . . .
I do like living on a boat.

25

TEXAS TRAINS AND TRAILS
Mary Austin

Whenever I ride on the Texas plains
I never hear the couplings cluck,
I never hear the trains
Go chuck-a-luck, chuck-a-luck, chuck-a-luck,
I never hear the engine snort and snuffle,
I never see the smoke plume, I never watch the rails,
But I see the moving dust where the beef herds shuffle,
And I think I am a cowboy,
A rope-and-tie-'em cowboy,
Punching Texas longhorns
On the Texas trails.

And the engine goes *Whoop!*
Whoopee, whoopala!
And the cars go *Ki-yi,*
Ki-yi, ki-yi, coma-la ki-yi,
    Whoopala
Ki-yi!
    Whoop!

No, I never hear the bell, nor the brakeman call
When I ride on the Texas trains;
But I hear the steers bellow and the yearlings bawl,
And the lone wolf howl on the wire-grass plains.
And I never play I'm fireman, nor anything like that,
For I'm playing I'm a cowboy,
A bronco-bustin' cowboy,
Riding Texas longhorns
In a ten-gallon hat.

And the trains go *Youpi-ya,*
Get a-long, dogies,
Get a-long, get a-long,
Youpi-yi, youpi-ya,
Youpi-youpi-youpi-ya,
Get a-long, get a-long,
Youpi-ya,
    Y-o-o-u-u-p!

SONG FOR A BLUE ROADSTER
Rachel Field

Fly, Roadster, fly!
  The sun is high,
Gold are the fields
  We hurry by,
Green are the woods
  As we slide through,
Past harbor and headland,
  Blue on blue.

Fly, Roadster, fly!
  The hay smells sweet,
And the flowers are fringing
  Each village street,
Where carts are blue,
  And barns are red,
And the road unwinds
  Like a twist of thread.

Fly, Roadster, fly!
  Leave Time behind;
Out of sight
  Shall be out of mind.
Shine and shadow,
  Blue sea, green bough,
Nothing is real
  But Here and Now.

HEADLIGHTS
Carolyn Forsyth

Over the back of the crouching hill,
  Over the hump of the night,
The automobiles, with squeaks and squeals,
  Keep lifting their eyes of light.

They seem like animal eyes in the dark
  That are stealthily searching for prey;
And the road is afraid for it wriggles its tail
  And hurriedly slithers away . . .

ON THE FARM
Anne Pérez-Guerra

Horses in the pasture lot,
   A windmill whirling 'round,
Apples on the orchard trees
   Tumbling to the ground,
Cattle grazing 'long the road,
   Porkers in a pen,
Chickens scratching near a coop
   Where lives the mother hen.
Sliding down a stack of straw,
   Jumping in the hay,
When I'm on the farm, I go
   Barefoot all the day.

FAREWELL TO THE FARM
Robert Louis Stevenson

The coach is at the door at last;
The eager children, mounting fast
And kissing hands, in chorus sing:
Good-bye, good-bye, to everything!

To house and garden, field and lawn,
The meadow-gates we swung upon,
To pump and stable, tree and swing,
Good-bye. good-bye, to everything!
    . . . .

Crack goes the whip, and off we go;
The trees and houses smaller grow;
Last round the woody turn we swing:
Good-bye, good-bye, to everything!

I'D LIKE TO BE A LIGHTHOUSE
Rachel Field

I'd like to be a lighthouse
　　All scrubbed and painted white.
I'd like to be a lighthouse
　　And stay awake all night
To keep my eye on everything
　　That sails my patch of sea;
I'd like to be a lighthouse
　　With ships all watching me.

MRS. BROWN

Rose Fyleman

As soon as I'm in bed at night
And snugly settled down,
The little girl I am by day
Goes very suddenly away,
And then I'm Mrs. Brown.

I have a family of six,
And all of them have names,
The girls are Joyce and Nancy Maude,
The boys are Marmaduke and Claude
And Percival and James.

We have a house with twenty rooms
A mile away from town;
I think it's good for girls and boys
To be allowed to make a noise—
And so does Mr. Brown.

We do the most exciting things,
Enough to make you creep,
And on and on and on we go—
I sometimes wonder if I know
When I have gone to sleep.

THE HARPERS' FARM
Dorothy Aldis

We always drive along until
We reach a certain little hill,
And on the other side of this
The farm should be and there it is,
Waiting for us, white and neat
In the misty summer heat.
And here we are and here we are,
Climbing quickly from the car
And asking may we ride the horse,
And Mrs. Harper says: "Of course."
And asking are there any new
Kittens, and she says: "A few."
And asking may we go and play
Hide-and-Seek up in the hay.
And in a corner of the loft
There ARE the kittens gray and soft,
With tongues just learning how to drink
And little ears all lined with pink.
Then Mrs. Harper calls: "Yoo hoo!"
And so we run (we always do)
Out of the barn and through a gate
And find some cookies on a plate,

Sugar on the top and cut
Like stars, and each one with a nut.
And there is also lemonade
In a pitcher in the shade.
And after that we always climb
On Bessie's back one at a time,
And Mrs. Harper laughs at us,
But it seems very dangerous.
We squeal and grab each other's clothes,
We hang on with our knees and toes
And say "Giddap," and Bessie does,
And such a gallop never was!
Then we get off her all alone,
Her tail a rope for sliding down.
And soon it's late and time to go
So we tell Mrs. Harper so.
"Thanks for the lemonade," we say
And wave good-bye. And drive away.

OUR STREET

Gertrude Strickler

Our street has houses in a row,
And when I'm walking to and fro,
Each house will look at me and say
A greeting to me, in its way.

There's one that always wears a smile
And seems to say, "Come in a while."
Another looks demurely down
And yet another wears a frown.

There's one whose mouth and window-eyes
Are opened wide in great surprise.
There's one that looks so fierce and bold—
It's like a pirate man of old.

But at the end of all the row
Is where I like the best to go,
For there's a house that's young and gay.
It says, "Come in my yard and play."

A NEW FRIEND

Marjorie Allen Anderson

They've taken in the furniture;
I watched them carefully.
I wondered, "Will there be a child
Just right to play with me?"

So I peeked through the garden fence
(I couldn't wait to see).
I found the little boy next door
Was peeking back at me.

SWINGING

Marjorie Allen Anderson

Here we go swinging,
To the tree top,
Here we go singing,
Don't let us stop.

Like a bird winging
Through the blue sky,
Here we go swinging
Dolly and I.

HAPPY DAY

Betty Jump

This whole long day was merry.
I saw a bluebird's nest;
I stroked a furry kitten
And passed my spelling test.

I watched the glowing sunset,
All rosy in the west,
But reading in the lamplight
Was the time that I loved best.

GARDEN FANCY

Mildred Bowers Armstrong

Our garden has a little pool
Where flowers often like to cool
Their faces that the sun has flushed,
Or look to see if their hats are brushed.
And every flower the garden grows
Puts pollen*powder* on her nose.

MY TEDDY BEAR

Louise de Marigny Smith
[Written when age thirteen]

I have a little Teddy Bear.
He's as old as he can be.
Though I squash him when I sleep at night,
I think he's fond of me.

His eyes are hanging by a thread,
His stuffing's coming out,
But still he sits upon my bed
And never seems to pout.

He comforts me when I am sad.
He gives me good advice.
I think my little Teddy Bear
Is awfully, awfully nice.

MORNING EXERCISES

Ruth Crary

Silver poplars reach upwards in rows,
And the maple tree bends as it blows.
   With the tips of their fingers
   Where still water lingers,
Weeping willows are touching their toes.

ACORNS*

Edith King

Oh, when the ripe acorns,
So smooth and so brown,
Get loose from their cups
And come pattering down,

What work is in store
For the girls and the boys,
First of all to collect them,
And then to make toys.

For they can make thimbles,
And tiny dolls' cradles,
And thorn-handled saucepans,
And egg-cups and ladles,

Extinguishers, flower-pots,
Baskets and rings,
And barrels and buckets,
And all kinds of things.

They can stock a whole shop,
If they have any brains,
And use a small penknife,
And plenty of pains.

MERRY–GO–ROUND

Marguerite Gode

Round and round
Goes the merry-go-round.
The music is churning
An organ-sweet sound,
While horses and tigers
And zebras and bears
Go galloping, galloping
Onward in pairs.

*"Acorns" from *Fifty Country Rhymes for Children*, by E. L. M. King. Copyright, 1926, D. Appleton & Company. Reprinted by permission of Appleton-Century-Crofts, Inc.

The tall ticket taker
Walks, leaning our way,
And laughs at a clown
In his pantaloons gay.
The thin man and midget
Stand there side by side
To wave at the children
Enjoying their ride.

Slower . . . and slower
. . . And slower we go
Slower . . .
And slower . . .
The music runs low.
Down from the horses
We slide to the ground
And feel very queer
As we stagger around.

THE PLAYHOUSE KEY
Rachel Field

This is the key to the playhouse
   In the woods by the pebbly shore,
It's winter now: I wonder if
   There's snow about the door?

I wonder if the fir trees tap
   Green fingers on the pane;
If sea gulls cry and the roof is wet
   And tinkle-y with rain?

I wonder if the flower-sprigged cups
   And plates sit on their shelf.
And if my little painted chair
   Is rocking by itself?

35

ATTIC TRUNK

Polly Chase

Hidden deep in attic dust,
Stands a trunk that creaks with rust.
I throw the cover open wide
To see what I can find inside.

First a dress of rose and gold,
Which I shall have when I am old;
Next a single scarlet shoe,
And then a scarf of peacock blue.

Outside the chilly fall wind blows
But I parade in glittering clothes.
Oh, rainy days are never dull!
And I am very beautiful!

THE LONG–AGO DOLL

Marjorie Barrows

'Way up in Grandma's attic where
  Some dusty little shadows creep,
I found my mother's Mandy Claire
  Inside a trunk asleep.

Her yellow dress was trimmed with lace,
  Her hair was very black and thin,
And camphor balls were in the place
  That she was dreaming in.

And long ago . . . and long ago . . .
  A little girl that used to be
Left Mandy Claire a-sleeping so—
  Before there was a me.

So Mandy Claire is waiting till . . .
  But I got sort of lonesome then
And while she slept there very still
  I tiptoed out again.

RADIO WISH

Ruth Dixon

I'd love to tune into the air
If I could hear instead
Of jazz-songs just a cricket's prayer
Before he goes to bed.

And then I'd tune and tune and tune
Till I heard way up far
The lullaby of Mother Moon
To a baby star.

SILVER

Walter de la Mare

Slowly, silently, now the moon
Walks the night in her silver shoon;
This way, and that, she peers, and sees
Silver fruit upon silver trees;
One by one the casements catch
Her beams beneath the silvery thatch;
Couched in his kennel, like a log,
With paws of silver sleeps the dog;
From their shadowy cote the white breasts peep
Of doves in a silver-feathered sleep;
A harvest mouse goes scampering by,
With silver claws, and silver eye;
And moveless fish in the water gleam,
By silver reeds in a silver stream.

NIGHT

William Blake

The sun descending in the west,
The evening star does shine;
The birds are silent in their nest,
And I must seek for mine.
The moon like a flower
In heaven's high bower,
With silent delight,
Sits and smiles on the night. . . .

38

NORTH COUNTRY

Agnes Louise Dean

My father tells tales
  Of a country new to me,
Where his father has a house
  And a little ash tree,

Where the colors of a lake
  Change from amethyst to jade;
Where the partridge and the deer
  Go about unafraid,

Where the pines brush the stars;
  Where moonlight on the sand
Holds the water of the lake
  In a curved silver band.

By the time, my father says,
  That the little ash tree
Is red-gold with berries,
  He will journey there with me.

HAPPILY EVER AFTER

Adelaide Love

"Happily ever after" are
The merriest sounding words!
The shining brook that travels far
Might sing them, or the birds.

I think of jolly little bells
When I hear Mother say
(The fairy stories that she tells
Always end that way)
    "Happily ever after,
    Happily ever after!"

AIR MAIL

Gordon Hillman

Every night when the clock strikes eight
And the stars are out and it's very late,
And the moon is dim in the western sky
I watch to see the mail go by.

You can hear it whirring over the hill
When the sun has set and the wind is still,
And if you are looking straight overhead
You see its lights all green and red,

And its motor plays a little tune
As a shadow swoops across the moon.
Just beneath the stars and across the sky,
I watch the mail go roaring by.

TRAINS AT NIGHT

Frances Frost

I like the whistle of trains at night,
The fast trains thundering by so proud!
They rush and rumble across the world,
They ring wild bells and they toot so loud!

But I love better the slower trains.
They take their time through the world instead,
And whistle softly and stop to tuck
Each sleepy blinking town to bed!

GUESTS

Marguerite Gode

Brown bread toasting,
Apples roasting,
Kitchen warm and bright,
Kettle singing,
Doorbell ringing,
We have guests tonight!

THE BAD KITTENS

Elizabeth Coatsworth

You may call, you may call,
But the little black cats won't hear you;
The little black cats are maddened
By the bright green light of the moon.
They are running and whirling and hiding,
They are wild who were once so confiding,
They are mad when the moon is riding—
You will not catch the kittens soon!

They care not for saucers of milk;
They care not for pillows of silk;
Your softest, crooningest call
Means less than the buzzing of flies.
They are seeing more than you see,
They are hearing more than you hear,
And out of the darkness they peer,
With a goblin light in their eyes!

THE MAGIC SCREEN

Bertha Ten Eyck James

The screen beside my bed is tall and black,
  'Broidered with full-rigged ships asail
    from distant shore.
This one is going to Mombasa town,
  And this to Singapore.

And this one here, with golden prow upturned,
  Seeks treasure in a lazy southern sea,
This with gray sail brings softest northern furs,
  This orange one returns from Sicily.

Across the magic screen at night,
  To many ports I sail my ships,
But every day they anchor here,
  So no one knows about their trips.

41

THE SPECTACLES

Fredrika Shumway Smith

My Granny lost her spectacles,
And when she went to bed
I peeked at her and there they were,
On top of Granny's head!

I took them gently in my hand
And stood high on my toes,
And then I held my breath real tight
And put them on her nose.

My Granny did not wake at all,
She only winked one eye,
And so, I guess, perhaps she thought
That I was just a fly!

MY HOUSE

Adelaide Love

I think my house is the nicest house
There is in the world, don't you?
It has a big back yard with a swing,
And a little front yard, too.

It has an attic where I can hide,
And a closet under the stair;
I never leave my toys in the yard
But carefully put them there.

It has a kitchen with smells I like
When I come in from play,
And my room upstairs where I build my blocks
Or draw on a rainy day.

It's green and white. Oh, I like my house
Much better than any other,
Because, whenever I come inside,
Why, there, you see, is my mother!

SONG FOR SUPPER

J. Lilian Vandevere

Baked potato, crackly brown,
Melted butter running down.
    But applesauce for supper
    Is what I like instead:
    Applesauce for supper
    And a slice of raisin bread.

Eggs all scrambled, piping hot,
Served with bacon, like as not.
    But applesauce for supper
    Is what I like the most:
    Applesauce for supper
    And a piece of crunchy toast.

Sometimes cocoa, hot and sweet,
Pudding for a special treat.
    But applesauce for supper
    Is what I like, don't you?
    Applesauce for supper
    And a ginger cookie, too!

REFLECTION

Eunice Tietjens

I'm glad I'm not the president
And very glad I'm not a king.
There's something grand about them, but
They're blamed for everything.

TRAINS

James S. Tippett

Over the mountains,
Over the plains,
Over the rivers,
Here come the trains.
Carrying passengers,
Carrying mail,
Bringing their precious loads
In without fail.
Thousands of freight cars
All rushing on
Through day and darkness
Through dusk and dawn.
Over the mountains,
Over the plains,
Over the rivers,
Here come the trains.

MOVING

Eunice Tietjens

I like to move. There's such a feeling
Of hurrying and scurrying,
And such a feeling of men with trunks
    and packing cases,
Of kitchen clocks and mother's laces,
Dusters, dishes, books, and vases,
Toys and pans and candles.
I always find things I'd forgotten:
An old brown Teddy stuffed with cotton,
Some croquet mallets without handles,
A marble and my worn-out sandals,
A half an engine and a hat. . . .
And I like that.
I like to watch the big vans backing,
And the lumbering and the cumbering,
And the hammering and the tacking.
I even like the packing.
And that will prove
I like to move!

44

RANGER WISHES
Kate Cox Goddard

I wish I had a pair of boots,
A pair that just fits *me;*
A saddle I can sit upon
To ride the wide prairie;
A gun that shoots, and spurs and chaps
To cross the mountains stony;
And while I tell I might as well
Be wishing for a pony.

SANTA FE, NEW MEXICO
Polly Chase

There are jack rabbits and prairie dogs
　Out west where the sidewalk ends,
And Indians and Mexicans—
　And they are all my friends.

But when the moon comes sliding
　And sagebrush turns to foam,
Then outdoors is Out West,
　But indoors is home.

45

GALLANTRY BOWER

Agnes Louise Dean

Gallantry Bower, Gallantry Bower!
We're going to start in a quarter 'v an hour!

It's a dangerous walk, I am glad to say.
The path hugs the cliff's edge most of the way;
Mother holds my hand, and I let her grab it
When I lean out over to see a rabbit.
Rabbits can frisk down the cliff to the sea,
But it's out of the question for Mother and me.

Gallantry Bower, Gallantry Bower!
We're going to start in a quarter 'v an hour!

There's a little stone house which I like to pretend
Is an Ogre's castle (but I am his friend)
And beyond is a sort of pagoda seat
Where the spreading wings of four angels meet,
Both excellent shelters in case of a shower,
But the best place to stop is Gallantry Bower.

Gallantry Bower is high and bare,
Hundreds of fields can be seen from there;
Hundreds of sheep, and grazing cows;
And furrows of red where the farmer plows.

Gallantry Bower is the top of the world,
Where a few old trees, witch-twisted and knurled
Wait, circle-wise, in the wind, for a chance
To whirl in a ring-around-rosy dance.

Oh, I simply adore it at Gallantry Bower!
And we're going to start in a quarter 'v an hour!

MEXICAN PALM

Emilie Fendall Johnson

My tree is like a duster reaching high,
Stretching forth to sweep the cloudy sky.
My tree is thin and mostly trunk, it's true,—
But oh, my tree, it has a lovely view!

GOOSE
Ruth Dixon

All by himself he flies along
Way up above our tallest spruce,
And sings a little honking song
To show he's glad to be a goose.

MY NEW ROLLER SKATES
Fleur Conkling

My legs go in
My legs go out;
Myself is turned
Just all about.

My feet fly up
Far from the ground.
The street is up
And can't be found.

The sky is down
Beneath my feet,
And sidewalks are
A hard, hard seat.

TIDY TURTLE
Polly Chase

My turtle is a tidy boy!
When he is tired of play,
He folds himself up carefully,
And puts himself away.

47

THE CIRCUS
Mary Beimfohr

Oh, I went to the circus hippity hop,
And not one time did I want to stop.

But I went home feeling queer and proud;
I didn't want to speak out loud,

For better than animal things to see
Was the funny clown. He walked with ME.

MY CROOKED OLD HOUSE
Lorena La Brec Ouellette

I live in the top of a crooked old house
Which sets tipsy-tilt on a hill.

A sly old cat and a beady-eyed mouse
Play chase-and-catch in my crooked old house

While an owl with a crooked bill
Hoots, loud hoots from the window sill,

And winky-winks at my speckled-plumed grouse
Who lives loft-high in my crooked old house.

Then I, with a spin and a spill,
Dance a lop-sided gay quadrille

With the cat, the mouse, the owl, and the grouse
In the top tip-top of my crooked old house.

48

THE MUMPS

Elizabeth Madox Roberts

I had a feeling in my neck,
And on the sides were two big bumps,
I couldn't swallow anything
At all because I had the mumps.

And Mother tied it with a piece,
And then she tied up Will and John,
And no one else but Dick was left
That didn't have a mump rag on.

He teased at us and laughed at us,
And said whenever he went by,
"It's vinegar and lemon drops
And pickles!" just to make us cry.

But Tuesday Dick was very sad
And cried because his neck was sore,
And not a one said sour things
To anybody any more.

AT THE ZOO

Marjorie Allen Anderson

Camels are bumpy,
Their backs are all lumpy;
Giraffes are long-legged and meek;
Bears are so growly,
Hyenas are howly,
Sea lions are slippery and sleek.

Kangaroos have a pocket,
But no way to lock it;
Their babies can look out and peep;
But monkeys are funny;
I wish I had money—
Enough to buy one I could keep.

SPRING SIGNS

Mildred Bowers Armstrong

Everywhere the wind blows
There goes spring—
Red kites and blue kites
Are tugging at the string.

Walks have hardly dried
Until marbles roll about
Long before the colored flowers
In the fields are out.

Maybe there is frost yet
And a touch of snow,
But there are little spring-signs
Where the children go.

ON THE TRAIN

Ruth Dixon

I sit beside the windowpane
When I go riding on the train.
I squash my nose upon the glass
And watch the dusty houses pass;
I hear some little breezes whine
And tag the washing on the line;
And I see alley cats who blink
And hold their whiskers still and think.
They all can hear our engine cry,
But do they know *I'm* going by?

TIM

Nancy Byrd Turner

Tim longs for great adventures,
But he never can roam;
He's always finding silly things,
Tiny, wet, and chilly things,
And taking them home.

He wants to be a rover
And sail the wide foam,
But small, outrageous, hobbly things,
Exasperating, wobbly things
Are somehow always turning up
To keep him still at home.

ROADS

Rachel Field

A road might lead to anywhere—
    To harbor towns and quays,
Or to a witch's pointed house
    Hidden by bristly trees.
It might lead past the tailor's door,
    Where he sews with needle and thread,
Or by Miss Pim the milliner's,
    With her hats for every head.
It might be a road to a great, dark cave
    With treasure and gold piled high,
Or a road with a mountain tied to its end,
    Blue-humped against the sky.
Oh, a road might lead you anywhere—
    To Mexico or Maine.
But then, it might just fool you, and—
    Lead you back home again!

THE PIGEON

Marjorie Barrows

I meet him every single day
When I go past the keep-off ground,
He's very fat and blue and gray
And always turns around.

He turns upon his pigeon toes
And whispers just a little coo
As round and round and round he goes:
That's all he likes to do.

And when I speak to him, why he
Just stops and stares and stares, and then
He nods a howdy-do to me
And turns around again.

WHICH?

Joyce L. Brisley

Whenever I'm walking in the wood
I'm never certain whether I should
Shuffle along where the dead leaves fall
Or walk as if I'm not there at all.

It's nice to rustle as hard as you can,
But I can't decide if it's nicer than
Creeping along, while the woodbirds call,
Pretending you are not there at all!

IF I WERE OTHERWISE

Joyce L. Brisley

If I were very, very tall, as tall as I could be,
I'd play with all the little birds up in the topmost tree;
I'd jump right over houses and think nothing of a wall,
If I were very, very, very, very, very tall!

If I were very, very small, as small as I could be,
I'd run among the blades of grass where you
    could scarcely see,
I'd play with ants and beetles and I know I'd love them all,
If I were very, very, very, very, very small!

BELONGINGS

Marchette Chute

I've got a box
Where I keep my socks
And my tops and my ties and my jacks,
And marbles and glue
And a horse's shoe
And a lot of shiny tacks.

I've an arrowhead
And a chunk of lead
And a clock that works with springs.
I'm glad it's a box
That really locks,
It's so full of important things.

POLICEMEN ON PARADE

Jimmy Garthwaite

BRRROOM!
Brroom!
Broom—Broom—Broom!
Brroomety-oomety—boompty—
Brroomety-oompety—B O O M !
The policemen are out on parade today
And there's nothing that's nearly so grand
As the sight of them all as they swagger and sway
To the sound of their wonderful band!

SUZIE

53

THE CARAVAN

Madeleine Nightingale

If I could be a gipsy-boy and have a caravan
I'd travel all the world, I would, before I was a man;
We'd drive beyond the far blue hills—us two, my horse and me—
And on and on and on and on until we reached the sea.

And there I'd wash his legs quite clean and bid him come inside,
Whilst I would stand upon the roof and scan the flowing tide,
And he and I would sail away and scour the Spanish main,
And when we'd swept the Spaniards out we'd p'r'aps sail home again.

Or if my horse was very tired of ships and being good,
And wanted most to stretch his legs (as many horses would)
We'd call a whale to tow us to a desert island beach,
And there we'd search for coconuts and have a whole one each.

If I could be a gipsy-boy I wouldn't bring a load
Of pots and pans and chairs and things and sell them in the road.
Oh, if I was a gipsy-boy and had a caravan
I'd see the whole wide world, I would, before I was a man.

THE PIRATE

Siddie Joe Johnson

I have been a pirate bold, and I have been a sailor,
And I have sailed my swing-boat to some ancient sea-song's measure.
I had for my companions a princess and a tailor,
And swung across the Front Yard Sea to search for buried treasure.

We moored upon the Back Yard Isle, and climbed the Henhouse
  Mountain
To spy the land for cross-marked trees and pirates worse than we.
I saw a palm a-waving; and the princess found a fountain;
And the tailor saw a cross-mark on the old mulberry tree.

The tree was low and shady, and the berries black and sweet.
We dug and dug with shovels until we could dig no more.
We found a wooden dagger; we found a gay tin fleet;
We found a little teapot—where we'd hidden them before.

54

BIRTHDAYS

Marchette Chute

We had waffles-with-syrup for breakfast,
As many as we could hold;
And I had some presents extra,
Because I am six years old.

I've thanked everyone for my presents,
And kissed 'em, and now that that's done
The family's all ready to do things,
Whatever I think would be fun.

When Timothy had his birthday
We went to the circus, and Tim
Laughed so hard at the seals and the monkeys
That a real clown winked at him.

And Dorothy chose a picnic
On the shores of a little lake,
With tadpoles, and buns, and diving,
And a four-layer birthday cake.

And now that it's my turn for choosing,
I'm going to ask if we might
Take all our family of rabbits
To bed with us just for tonight.

THE EASTER BUNNY
Louise de Marigny Smith
[Written when age seven]

Hop, hop, hop
Goes the Easter Bunny;
Hop, hop, hop,
From door to door.
All there is, in the dawn
of the morning,
all there is, is
Snore, Snore, Snore.
Busy little Easter Bunny;
Now it's almost day;
Busy working, busy working,
Eggs are on the way.

INDIAN BOY
Johnny Sloan
[Written when age fourteen]

All day the Indian boy
Watches his sheep.
The young lambs run,
The young lambs leap.
The boy sits dreaming
All day long,
His sheep his friends,
The wind his song.

THE MOUNTAIN
Caroline P. Wild
[Written when age eleven]

High and majestic the mountain stood
O'erlooking the fields and plains,
High and majestic the mountain stood
Through snows and sleets and rains.
High and majestic the mountain stood
Looking out to the gray-blue sea,
High and majestic the mountain stood
And oh, what a very small me.

LITTLE GIRL NEXT DOOR

Mildred Bowers Armstrong

If she had a broom straw
Stuck into her hat,
We'd think it was a feather—
She's like that.

WISHES

Edith Franklin Wyatt

I'm just myself; and when I see
The sparrows flying from a tree
And darting off up towards the sky,
Oh, how I wish that I could fly,
And were a bird, and not just me.
Or if I were a honeybee,
Sipping petunias happily,
I'd have more fun than now when I am just myself.
The stars come out. The winds blow free.
My mother comes and kisses me.
My father hugs me to him tight.
"Good night, dear sleepyhead, good night."
And then I'm very glad to be just myself.

CROSS–STITCH SAMPLER

Marion Strobel

We'll make a cross-stitch sampler now the rain
Is colder and there's frost upon the pane.
We'll make a house of colored thread that will
Have summer always on the window sill—
Its path will lead us where petunias are,
Its porch to shadows and a door ajar.
Throughout the winter somewhere overhead
Summer shall hang in stitches blue and red.

57

THE HOME–MADE SHIP
Carolyn Forsyth

I made a little sailing ship
  All on an August day
And sailed it in the meadow where
  I always like to play;
For meadowlands and fields can be
  As green as any lake or sea
And all the little winds that pass
  Put waves and ripples in the grass . . . .

And so I made a sailing ship
  For sailing far and fast.
The hull was just a packing-box,
  A yardstick was the mast.
The sail was just a worn out shirt
  That flapped before the blast.

But, oh, I took such happy trips!
  My travel was unending,
For anyone can travel when
  He's playing and pretending;
And since the seashore's far away
  And far off is the sand
I'll do my sailing here upon
  A bit of meadowland.

THE HOLLOW TREE HOUSE
Margaret Widdemer

I took my mother's parasol
  (But mother didn't mind)
One day when I'd been very good,
And went a journey in the wood
  To see what I could find.

I felt a pleasant kind of lost,
  And everything was green,
For all the leaves shook round about
And kept the shiny sunlight out
  As if they were a screen.

I went to find a playhouse where
  My china dolls could be,
So down along the mossy ground
I hunted till at last I found
  A hollow in a tree:

I lined the hole with silver-foil
  And made an acorn chair,
And put my dollies there to sit
And then—they looked so glad of it—
  I left them sitting there:

I filled the hole with buttercups
  As tight as they would go
And fastened strips of bark across
And filled it up with fuzzy moss
  So nobody could know.

But some day when I'm very old
  Some little girl like me
Will find my dollies all alone
A-sitting on their acorn throne
  Inside the hollow tree;

And I shall ride along in rings
  And satins, grand and slow,
And say to her, "I put them there
And left them on their acorn chair
  A long, long while ago!"

SNIFF

Frances Frost

When school is out we love to follow
our noses over hill and hollow,
smelling jewelweed and vetch,
sniffing fern and milkweed patch.

The airy fifth of our five senses
leads us under, over fences.
We run like rabbits through bright hours
and poke our noses into flowers.

VACATION TIME

Ann Zelenka

I wonder how the schoolhouse feels
    Now everyone has gone;
Whether it likes to be left alone
    From dawn to rosy dawn.

I think . . . perhaps . . . it does, for now
    The wind is cool and sweet,
The grasses green and clover-starred,
    Untrodden by careless feet.

The noise and clamor are far away,
    There is a silence in the hall—
Only the whisper of sunlit leaves
    As they rustle against the wall.

SELF–CONTROL
Polly Chase

My dolly would not play with me.
She simply stared
Her silly stare.
It made me *wild*
To pull her hair.

I kissed her *very quietly*
And walked outdoors and kicked a tree.

GENERAL STORE
Rachel Field

Some day I'm going to have a store
With a tinkly bell hung over the door,
With real glass cases and counters wide
And drawers all spilly with things inside.
There'll be a little of everything:
Bolts of calico; balls of string;
Jars of peppermint; tins of tea;
Pots and kettles and crockery;
Seeds in packets; scissors bright;
Kegs of sugar, brown and white;
Sarsaparilla for picnic lunches,
Bananas and rubber boots in bunches.
I'll fix the window and dust each shelf,
And take the money in all myself.
It will be my store and I will say:
"What can I do for you today?"

BALLOON

Ruth Dixon

My Daddy bought me a balloon
  From the balloon man in the park
Before the night turned on the moon
  To light the dark.

It let me pull it to our hill,
  And I held tight onto the string;
And hung it in the sky as still
  As anything.

But when some little breezes blew
  It tugged and tugged, so I would know
Just what it wanted me to do;
  Then I let go.

And up and up into the sky
  I saw it flying very far
And knew that my balloon would try
  To reach a star.

MY DOG

Marchette Chute

His nose is short and scrubby;
　His ears hang rather low;
And he always brings the stick back,
　No matter how far you throw.

He gets spanked rather often
　For things he shouldn't do,
Like lying-on-beds, and barking,
　And eating up shoes when they're new.

He always wants to be going
　Where he isn't supposed to go.
He tracks up the house when it's snowing—
　Oh, puppy, I love you so!

THE FRIENDLY PUP

Arthur Guiterman

When we go out to walk or run,
My little dog is full of fun
　And tugs so hard that though I'm strong
　He nearly pulls me right along.
　　He leaps and frisks or trots and jogs
　　And stops to talk with other dogs;
　　　And when they're big, though he is small,
　　　That doesn't scare my dog at all.
Because he's friendly through and through,
The other dogs are friendly, too.
　When people smile, he understands;
　They pat his head, he licks their hands;
　　They laugh to watch us romping by,
　　And we laugh back, my dog and I.

SLEIGH BELLS AT NIGHT

Elizabeth Coatsworth

There are no bells in all the world
so sweet as sleigh bells over snow.
The horses arch their necks to hear
that pretty music as they go.

If it is dark, you cannot see
the horses curvetting and prancing,
but you would know to hear the bells
that those who shook them must be dancing.

SAMMY SNOWMAN

Ruth Dixon

Funny Sammy Snowman,
    Big and cold and fat,
Here's a pipe and here's a cane
    And here's a queer old hat.

Here's a big umbrella
    And some mittens, too.
And to keep you nice and warm
    Here's a coat for you.

Boys and girls all like you,
    Birds see you and sing;
Funny Sammy Snowman,
    I hope you last till Spring!

SKATING

Herbert Asquith

When I try to skate,
My feet are so wary
They grit and grate;
And then I watch Mary
Easily gliding,
Like an ice-fairy;
Skimming and curving,
Out and in,
With a turn of her head,
And a lift of her chin,
And a gleam of her eye,
And a twirl and a spin;
Sailing under
The breathless hush
Of the willows, and back
To the frozen rush;
Out to the island
And round the edge,
Skirting the rim
Of the crackling sedge,
Swerving close
To the poplar root,
And round the lake
On a single foot,
With a three, and an eight,
And a loop and a ring;
Where Mary glides,
The lake will sing!
Out in the mist
I hear her now
Under the frost
Of the willow-bough
Easily sailing,
Light and fleet,
With the song of the lake
Beneath her feet.

THE SECRET CAVERN
Margaret Widdemer

Underneath the boardwalk, way, way back,
There's a splendid cavern, big and black—
If you want to get there, you must crawl
Underneath the posts and steps and all,
When I've finished paddling, there I go—
None of all the other children know!

There I keep my treasures in a box—
Shells and colored glass and queer-shaped rocks,
In a secret hiding-place I've made,
Hollowed out with clamshells and a spade,
Marked with yellow pebbles in a row—
None of all the other children know!

It's a place that makes a splendid lair,
Room for chests and weapons and one chair.
In the farthest corner, by the stones,
I shall have a flag with skulls and bones
And a lamp that casts a lurid glow—
None of all the other children know!

Some time, by and by, when I am grown,
I shall go and live there all alone;
I shall dig and paddle till it's dark,
Then go out and man my pirate bark:
I shall fill my cave with captive foe—
None of all the other children know!

THE HUT
Hilda van Stockum

We built a hut, my brother and I,
Over a sandy pit,
With twigs that bowed and met above
And leaves to cover it.

And there we sat when all around
The rain came pouring down.
We knew if we were out in it
We'd both be sure to drown.

And though in puddles at our feet
Drops gathered from the sky,
We smiled through strands of dripping hair,
Because we felt so dry.

SILVER SHIPS

Mildred Plew Meigs

There are trails that a lad may follow
　　When the years of his boyhood slip,
But I shall soar like a swallow
　　On the wings of a silver ship,

Guiding my bird of metal,
　　One with her throbbing frame,
Floating down like a petal,
　　Roaring up like a flame;

Winding the wind that scatters
　　Smoke from the chimney's lip,
Tearing the clouds to tatters
　　With the wings of a silver ship;

Grazing the broad blue sky light
　　Up where the falcons fare,
Riding the realms of twilight,
　　Brushed by a comet's hair;

Snug in my coat of leather,
　　Watching the skyline swing,
Shedding the world like a feather
　　From the tip of a tilted wing.

There are trails that a lad may travel
　　When the years of his boyhood wane,
But I'll let a rainbow ravel
　　Through the wings of my silver plane.

I CAUGHT A FISH

Dorothy Aldis

I caught a fish and I
Gave it to my father.
He took it and he cooked it
And he said he'd rather
Eat my fish
Than any other fishes,
And when he had tasted it
He said: "That was delicious."
And there wasn't ANY left
On either of our dishes.

IT WAS

Dorothy Aldis

When he came to tuck me in
And pat me on the head,
He tried to guess (the way he does)
Who was in my bed.

"Is it Sally?" he guessed first,
"Or her sister Joan?
It's such a wriggling little girl
It couldn't be my own.

"It can't be Alice Clay," he said,
"Or Deborah, because
All their eyes are much too blue—
My goodness me, I think it's you!"
And he was right. It was.

AWAY WE GO

Aileen Fisher

Mother plays a march
    And so
Away we go, away we go . . .
Past a forest made of chairs,
Up the mountain of the stairs,
Past a den of bears . . .
    And so
Away we go, away we go.

Music makes us march,
    You know,
Away we go, away we go . . .
Nancy with a paper cap
And Edward with a haversack
And Bunny at the back,
    And so
Away we go, away we go.

Houses may be small,
    But oh,
Away we go, away we go . . .
Through the cavern of the door,
Over meadows on the floor,
Over hills galore . . .
    And so
Away we go, away we go.

69

CHRISTMAS MORNING

Elizabeth Madox Roberts

If Bethlehem were here today,
Or this were very long ago,
There wouldn't be a wintertime
Nor any cold or snow.

I'd run out through the garden gate,
And down along the pasture walk;
And off beside the cattle barns
I'd hear a kind of gentle talk.

I'd move the heavy iron chain
And pull away the wooden pin;
I'd push the door a little bit
And tiptoe very softly in.

The pigeons and the yellow hens
And all the cows would stand away;
Their eyes would open wide to see
A lady in the manger hay,

If this were very long ago
And Bethlehem were here today.

And Mother held my hand and smiled—
I mean the lady would—and she
Would take the woolly blankets off
Her little boy so I could see.

His shut-up eyes would be asleep,
And he would look like our John,
And he would be all crumpled too,
And have a pinkish color on.

70

Pelagie Doane

I'd watch his breath go in and out.
His little clothes would all be white.
I'd slip my finger in his hand
To feel how he could hold it tight.

And she would smile and say, "Take care,"
The mother, Mary, would, "Take care";
And I would kiss his little hand
And touch his hair.

While Mary put the blankets back
The gentle talk would soon begin.
And when I'd tiptoe softly out
I'd meet the wise men going in.

LONG, LONG AGO

Author Unknown

Winds thro' the olive trees
  Softly did blow,
Round little Bethlehem
  Long, long ago.

Sheep on the hillside lay
  Whiter than snow;
Shepherds were watching them,
  Long, long ago.

Then from the happy sky,
  Angels bent low,
Singing their songs of joy,
  Long, long ago.

For in a manger bed,
  Cradled we know,
Christ came to Bethlehem,
  Long, long ago.

THE SHEPHERD LEFT BEHIND

Mildred Plew Meigs

"The hour is late," the shepherds said,
  "And the miles are long to wind;
Do you stay here with the sheep, instead!"
  And they left the lad behind.
He heard their feet in the dark ravine,
  The drop of the sheepfold bars,
And then blue stillness flowed between
  The huddled sheep and stars.
He sat him down to wait for dawn,
  His crook across his knees,
And thought of the shepherds moving on
  Under the olive trees.
Herding his flocks in Palestine,
  He thought, that lad of old,
How some must follow the Angel's sign
  And some must tend the fold.
And as he mused he took his pipe—
  'Twas a shepherd's pipe he had—
And there, while the frosty stars grew ripe
  And shone on the shepherd lad,
The first sweet Christmas carol twined
  From the willow's slender stem—
Blown by the shepherd left behind
  To a Babe in Bethlehem.

PINE TREE SONG

Marjorie Barrows

Little pines upon the hill,
Sleeping in the moonlight still,
Are you dreaming now of me
Who bloomed into a Christmas tree?
Baby moons of gold and red
Cuddle close beside my head;
In my tangled leaves a string
Of fairy stars are glimmering;
While my arms, for girls and boys,
Blossom with a hundred toys.
O, little pines, it's fun to live
To be a Christmas tree—and give!

I'M WISHING THE WHOLE WORLD CHRISTMAS*

Annette Wynne

I'm wishing the whole world Christmas—
The children, the beasts, and the birds;
I'm wishing the whole world Christmas—
And I'd like to have magical words
To wish just the shining wish I would wish
In the Christmas words I would say,
For I'm wishing the whole world Christmas,
And joy on Christmas Day.

O, I'd need a pen to write golden,
The goldenest pen indeed,
To wish the whole world Christmas
For the happy children to read.
I'm wishing the whole world Christmas
And may the dear Lord be kind,
And send blessings down like snowflakes
For all of His children to find. . . .

*Reprinted by permission of the publishers, J. B. Lippincott Company, from *For Days and Days*, by Annette Wynne. Copyright, 1919, by J. B. Lippincott Company.

MY GIFT

Christina Rossetti

What can I give Him,
Poor as I am;
If I were a shepherd,
I would give Him a lamb.
If I were a wise man,
I would do my part.
But what can I give Him?
I will give Him my heart.

CHRISTMAS GIFTS

Ruth Dixon

The night was cool, the night was still,
  The desert sand was soft and white,
And there were stars up in the sky
  And one was bright.
And silently it shone upon
  The Wise Men as they rode along,
While in their hearts the Wise Men sang
  A Christmas song.
And when they reached the manger, there
  Was Mary with her new-born child,
And when He saw His gifts, I'm sure
  The Baby smiled.

THE FIRST NIGHT

Louise Ayres Garnett

The stable door was closed that night,
But through the cracks no bolts could bar
The light of holy innocence
Burst like a spraying star.
Even the beasts were glad He came.
They knelt in patience where He lay,
Content to yield for His baby head
Their evening meal of hay.

CHRISTMAS EVE

Ruth Dixon

On Christmas Eve before the moon
　　Turns on the stars to light the dark,
Our church bells chime a Christmas tune,
　　And we all gather in the park.
And in the snow we form a ring
　　Around a Christmas tree and then
We sing about the Newborn King
　　And Peace on Earth, Good Will Toward Men.
I hold hands with our bootblack's Joe
　　And sing and sing beside the tree
Of Bethlehem in Long-Ago. . . .
　　And I feel very Christmas-y.

EVER VERY NEAR

Author Unknown

Father, we thank thee for the night.
Keep us safe till morning light,
As the shepherd in his fold
Keeps his sheep from harm and cold.
Bless all friends to us so dear,
Father, Mother, and all here,
And may Thy little children be
Ever very near to Thee.

75

ABOUT CHRISTMAS
Adelaide Love

There's so much to love about Christmas!
The story that Mother tells
Of the Star and the Babe in the manger,
The songs and the Christmas bells;

The toys and the wreaths and the candles,
The snow and the company,
And oh, when you wake up on Christmas,
The smell of the Christmas tree!

CHRISTMAS SONG
Elizabeth-Ellen Long

Of all the animals on earth
I think the luckiest
Are the ox and ass who had
Young Jesus for their guest,
The ox and ass in Bethlehem
Whose privilege and joy
It was to share their stable with
A little homeless Boy.
The luckiest of animals
On earth, both tame and wild,
For they were first to look with love
Upon the Christmas Child!

FIRES
Agnes Louise Dean

The ottoman beside the fire is where I sit and think,
The heat makes me drowsy, the flames make me blink.

I think about the blazing logs which once were stately trees
With all their leaves a-dancing, dancing in the breeze,

Green in the Summertime, scarlet in the Fall,
With stars and snow at Christmas-Tide, most beautiful of all.

76

CHRISTMAS IN THE WOODS

Frances Frost

Tonight when the hoar frost falls on the wood,
And the rabbit cowers and the squirrel is cold,
And the horned owl huddles against a star,
And the drifts are deep and the year is old,
All shy creatures will think of Him.
The shivering mouse, the hare, the wild young fox,
The doe with the startled fawn,
Will dream of gentleness and a Child:

The buck with budding horns will turn
His starry eyes to a silver hill tonight,
The chipmunk will awake and stir
And leave his burrow for the chill, dark midnight,
And all timid things will pause and sigh, and sighing bless
That Child who loves the trembling hearts,
The shy hearts of the wilderness.

SHINE, STAR
Nancy Byrd Turner

Shine, star!
Shine on a stable of long ago,
Shine on a field in a land afar
That sheep and shepherds used to know,
Shine through the crystal, twilight air
While carols echo across the hill
And candles burn in each happy house
On table, mantel, and cedar boughs,
And every window sill.

Pour your beauty on town and plain,
On tower and spire, on open pine,
Drop your silver on street and lane,
On roof and gable and windowpane.
Shed your joy in this heart of mine
And other hearts wherever they are.
Shine, Christmas star!

MAUD—MISKA
PETERSHAM

MORNING

Ruth Dixon

The birds have washed their faces
   And cuddle in a row
Upon a little frosty bush
   That twinkles in the snow.

And up above our hilltop
   The sky is very blue,
And all the birds are singing now,
   And we are singing, too,

For everything's beginning
   Again today, so here
We wave our wings and hands and say
   Good morning to the year!

LINCOLN

Nancy Byrd Turner

There was a boy of other days,
A quiet, awkward, earnest lad,
Who trudged long weary miles to get
A book on which his heart was set—
And then no candle had!

He was too poor to buy a lamp
But very wise in woodmen's ways.
He gathered seasoned bough and stem,
And crisping leaf, and kindled them
Into a ruddy blaze.

Then as he lay full length and read,
The firelight flickered on his face,
And etched his shadow on the gloom,
And made a picture in the room,
In that most humble place.

The hard years came, the hard years went,
But, gentle, brave, and strong of will,
He met them all. And when today
We see his pictured face, we say,
"There's light upon it still."

VALENTINE TO MY DOLL
Helen Wing

I love you, dear, although I know
Your body is a rag.
We made you out of pieces from
My grandma's sewing bag.
Your legs are getting rather limp;
Your neck is wobbly too;
Yet no doll in the nursery
Is half so dear as you.

WASHINGTON
Nancy Byrd Turner

He played by the river when he was young,
He raced with rabbits along the hills,
He fished for minnows, and climbed and swung,
And hooted back at the whippoorwills.
Strong and slender and tall he grew
And then, one morning, the bugles blew.

Over the hills, the summons came,
Over the river's shining rim.
He said that the bugles called his name,
He knew that his country needed him,
And he answered, "Coming!" and marched away
For many a night and many a day.

Perhaps when the marches were hot and long
He'd think of the river flowing by,
Or, camping under the winter sky,
Would hear the whippoorwill's far-off song.
Boy and soldier, in peace or strife,
He loved America all his life!

81

PLANTING A TREE

Nancy Byrd Turner

Firm in the good brown earth
  Set we our little tree.
Clear dews will freshen it,
Cool rain will feed it,
Sun will be warming it
As warmth is needed.
Winds will blow round it free—
  Take root, good tree!

Slowly, as days go on,
  These boughs will stouter be,
Leaves will unfurl on them,
And, when spring comes to them,
Blossoms uncurl on them,
Birds make their homes in them,
Shade outstretch, wide and free—
  Grow well, good tree!

SING, WORLD, SING!

Nancy Byrd Turner

Now in chilly places
Where the snow had been,
Wood and field and hollow,
Easter flowers begin.

Now a bud is opened,
Now a leaf uncurled;
Spring is in the sweet wind
Walking down the world.

Snowdrops in the garden,
Violets on the hills,
Cowslips in the meadow,
Dancing daffodils

Seem to lift their faces,
Softly whispering,
*"Easter's nearly here, now—
Sing, world, sing!"*

ROUND THE MAY POLE NOW WE DANCE

Nancy Byrd Turner

Round the May Pole now we dance
(Over with blue, under with white),
Wind's in the ribbons, oh, see them lift!
Light's on the ribbons, oh, feel them shift!
While we braid overhead
Colors fair and bright!

Round the May Pole gay we move
(You with your ribbon, I with mine).
The colors cross and the pattern grows
(Over with red and under with rose).
On and on, till we're done.
See the tall pole shine!

OUR AMERICA

Ruth Dixon

America! America!
We'll sing our love for you
From prairie farms and mountain homes
And towered cities too.

O land of Washington and Lincoln,
Land of pioneers,
Our gratitude to you we'll show
Throughout the coming years!

Your stars and stripes wave in the breeze
And thrill us all today,
In God we trust, America,
He'll lead us on our way.

America, we'll work with you
For what we know is good,
We'll work for Truth and Liberty
And Peace and Brotherhood!

THE BIRTHDAY OF OUR LAND

Nancy Byrd Turner

The birthday of a lovely land!
Our flag is flying near and far;
The wind is rippling all its folds,
Color by color, star by star;
And music sounds, and songs begin—
Oh, bare the head and lift the hand!
It is a happy thing to be
A part of such a land.
The story of three hundred years
Is told again in streets and homes.
America, America—
Once more her birthday comes!

COLUMBUS

Joaquin Miller

Behind him lay the gray Azores,
    Behind the Gates of Hercules;
Before him not the ghost of shores,
    Before him only shoreless seas.

The good mate said: "Now must we pray,
    For lo! the very stars are gone.
Brave Admiral, speak, what shall I say?"
    "Why, say 'Sail on! sail on! and on!'"

"My men grow mutinous day by day;
    My men grow ghastly wan and weak."
The stout mate thought of home; a spray
    Of salt wave washed his swarthy cheek.
"What shall I say, brave Admiral, say,
    If we sight naught but seas at dawn?"
"Why, you shall say at break of day,
    'Sail on! sail on! sail on! and on!'"

They sailed and sailed, as winds might blow,
    Until at last the blanched mate said,
"Why, now not even God would know
    Should I and all my men fall dead.
These very winds forget their way,
    For God from these dread seas is gone.
Now speak, brave Admiral, speak and say"—
    He said: "Sail on! sail on! and on!"

They sailed. They sailed. Then spake the mate:
    "This mad sea shows his teeth tonight.
He curls his lips, he lies in wait,
    With lifted teeth, as if to bite!
Brave Admiral, say but one good word:
    What shall we do when hope is gone?"
The words leapt like a leaping sword:
    "Sail on! sail on! sail on! and on!"

Then, pale and worn, he kept his deck,
    And peered through darkness. Ah, that night
Of all dark nights! And then a speck—
    A light! a light! a light! a light!
It grew, a starlit flag unfurled!
    It grew to be Time's burst of dawn.
He gained a world; he gave that world
    Its grandest lesson: "On, sail on!"

THREE LITTLE WITCHES

Marjorie Barrows

One little, *two* little,
   Three little witches
Fly over haystacks,
   Fly over ditches,
Slide down the moon
   Without any hitches,
      Hey-ho! Halloween's here!

Horned owl's hooting it's
   Time to go riding!
Deep in the shadows are
   Black bats hiding,
With gay little goblins
   Sliding, gliding,
      Hey-ho! Halloween's here!

Stand on your head with a
   Lopsided wiggle,
Tickle your little black
   Cats till they giggle,
Swish through the clouds
   With a higgledy-piggle!
      Hey-ho! Halloween's here!

Dust off the silvery stars
   Till they're gleaming,
Down where the will-o'-wisp's
   Beckoning, beaming,
Dance in the dusk while the
   World lies dreaming,
      Hey-ho! Halloween's here!

One little, *two* little,
   Three little witches
Fly over haystacks,
   Fly over ditches,
Slide down the moon
   Without any hitches,
      Hey-ho! Halloween's here!

WITCH CAT

Rowena Bennett

I want a little witch cat
    With eyes all yellow-green,
Who rides upon a broomstick
    Every Halloween,
Who purrs when she is taking off,
    Just like a purring plane,
And doesn't mind a tailspin
    Even in the rain.

I want a cat who dares to light
    The candle of the moon
And set its jack-o-lantern face
    A-laughing like a loon.

I want a cat who laps the milk
    Along the Milky Way,
A cat of spunk and character
    As daring as the day;
But gentle-looking kittens
    Are in the stores to sell
And which cat is a witch cat,
    I really cannot tell.

HALLOWEEN
Helen Wing

We had a Goblin party on the night of Halloween,
And all the children on our street were there,
And it was dark inside our house with only candlelight,
And Jack-o'-lanterns standing by the stair.

There was a big, enormous Ghost that walked around the room
(The Ghost was really Father in a sheet),
And he made moans and shook his head, but no one was afraid!
Because he gave us lollipops to eat.

I dressed up like a Goblin in a last-year's Brownie suit
(I made myself a tail that I could wag);
And Mary Ann rode on a broom and was a kind of Witch
Who kept her magic secrets in a bag.

We bobbed for apples in a tub and caught them with our teeth,
But I got water in my nose and eyes,
So I was glad when Mother called us to the dining room,
For that was where we found the big surprise.

The table was more fancy than I'd ever seen before;
I couldn't tell what thing I liked the most,
The doughnuts or the pumpkin pie, the cider or ice cream,
All served to us by Mother and the Ghost.

When there was nothing left but crumbs, the children had to go
'Cause it was past their time to go to bed;
Then everybody thanked us for the party, and they wished
That Halloween came *every* week, they said.

GOBLIN GADGETS
Rowena Bennett

A gimcrack goblin and a knick-knack gnome
Have a little gadget shop, three steps from home.
Selling strange inventions like dandelion mops,
And daffodil dishes and acorn spinning tops.
They sell scrub brushes with sharp little bristles
Made of brown burrs or of blue-headed thistles.

But nobody can shop there (at least that's what I've heard)
Unless he's wearing feathers, like a fairy, or a bird.

FIRST THANKSGIVING OF ALL

Nancy Byrd Turner

    Peace and Mercy and Jonathan,
    And Patience (very small),
    Stood by the table giving thanks
    The first Thanksgiving of all.
There was very little for them to eat,
Nothing special and nothing sweet;
Only bread and a little broth,
And a bit of fruit (and no tablecloth);
    But Peace and Mercy and Jonathan
    And Patience, in a row,
    Stood up and asked a blessing on
    Thanksgiving, long ago.

    Thankful they were their ship had come
    Safely across the sea;
    Thankful they were for hearth and home,
    And kin and company;
They were glad of broth to go with their bread,
Glad their apples were round and red,
Glad of mayflowers they would bring
Out of the woods again next spring.
    So Peace and Mercy and Jonathan,
    And Patience (very small),
    Stood up gratefully giving thanks
    The first Thanksgiving of all.

THANKSGIVING
Judy Van der Veer

Outside the barn the wind is strong,
Bringing cold November rain;
Within these walls the hay is sweet,
Bins are filled with yellow grain.

The cows are quiet in their stalls,
The newest calf is sound asleep;
And close together in their pen
Rest the gently breathing sheep.

The mare's big colt is by her side
To share with her the golden hay—
I'm truly thankful, Lord, that these
Are fed and sheltered on this day.

INDIAN CHILDREN LONG AGO
Nancy Byrd Turner

Where we play in field and hill,
    Running high and low,
Other children used to play,
    Long and long ago.

Little Indians straight and slim,
    Boys with belt and feather,
Little girls with colored beads,
    Playing all together.

90

Laughing, calling through our yard
   (When 'twas field of maize)
Swift and light they used to run,
   Back in other days;

Through our garden (once a wood)
   In and out again,
Past the house they ran, and back—
   'Twas a wigwam then.

Sometimes when the air is clear,
   On a quiet day,
We can almost hear them still,
   Shouting at their play!

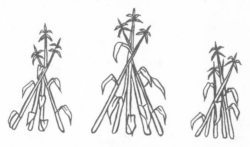

THANKSGIVING IS COMING
Elsie Melchert Fowler

Thanksgiving is coming, I wonder if I
Will get a big piece of brown pumpkin pie?

Perhaps I'll have sweet juicy mince pie instead,
And a big bowl of raisins and fat apples red.

"Do have my plum pudding," my grandma will say;
She always makes pudding for Thanksgiving Day.

But first I'll see turkey, breast up, on a platter,
I wonder if this year he's bigger and fatter?

When asked if I'd rather have dark meat or white
I'll say, "Some of both," for that's being polite!

Next potatoes, all mashed up with gravy on top.
I'll eat every bit of it up till I stop,

And after I've eaten my dinner, why then
My grandma will pass the plum pudding again!

91

Part III: ANIMAL PARADE

EYES ARE LIT UP
Robert P. Tristram Coffin

Someone whom no man can see
Is lighting candles in the tree.

Star by star, on every bough
There is a taper burning now.

Quietly, the forest through,
Eyes are lit up, two by two.

The silky moles and velvet mice
Have eyes as sharp as cracks of ice.

Dark-lanterns of the owls begin
To burn like emeralds and sin.

The raccoon built of hidden wire
Prowls by the glow of his brain-fire.

Herons stand as still as years
And see the fish swim through
    their tears.

All the creatures of the night
Are busy being their own light.

D.P.Lathrop

THE GRASSHOPPERS
Dorothy Aldis

High
Up
Over the top
Of feathery grasses the
Grasshoppers hop.
They won't eat their suppers;
They will not obey
Their grasshopper mothers
And fathers, who say:
"Listen, my children,
This must be stopped—
Now is the time your last
Hop should be hopped;
So come eat your suppers
And go to your beds—"
But the little green grasshoppers
Shake their green heads.
"No,
No—"
The naughty ones say,
"All we have time to do
Now is to play.
If we want supper we'll
Nip at a fly
Or nibble a blueberry
As we go by;
If we feel sleepy we'll
Close our eyes tight
And snoozle away in a
Harebell all night.
But not
Now.
Now we must hop.
And nobody,
NOBODY,
Can make us stop."

THE LITTLE TURTLE
Vachel Lindsay

There was a little turtle.
He lived in a box.
He swam in a puddle.
He climbed on the rocks.

He snapped at a mosquito.
He snapped at a flea.
He snapped at a minnow.
And he snapped at me.

He caught the mosquito.
He caught the flea.
He caught the minnow.
But he didn't catch me.

MICE
Rose Fyleman

I think mice
Are rather nice.
    Their tails are long,
    Their faces small,
    They haven't any
    Chins at all.
    Their ears are pink,
    Their teeth are white.
    They run about
    The house at night.
    They nibble things
    They shouldn't touch
    And no one seems
    To like them much.
But I think mice
Are nice.

SONG OF THE RABBITS
OUTSIDE THE TAVERN

Elizabeth Coatsworth

We who play under the pines,
We who dance in the snow
That shines blue in the light of the moon
Sometimes halt as we go,
Stand with our ears erect,
Our noses testing the air,
To gaze at the golden world
Behind the windows there.

Suns they have in a cave,
And stars each on a tall white stem
And the thought of fox or of owl
Seems never to bother them.
They laugh and eat and are warm,
Their food is ready at hand
While hungry out in the cold,
We little rabbits stand.

But they never dance as we dance,
They have not the speed nor the grace,
We scorn both the cat and the dog
Who lie by their fireplace,
We scorn them, licking their paws,
Their eyes on an upraised spoon—
We who dance hungry and wild
Under a winter's moon!

WOODCHUCK HILL

Frances Frost

I saw a baby woodchuck
Sitting on a knoll,
Blinking in the sunlight,
Fat and brown and droll.
He ate a head of clover,
And then he ate another,

But when he grabbed a big paw full,
Up popped his little brother.

His little brother squeaked,
And bumped and bowled him over!
They fought like infant furies
For a bunch of clover!
Then spanked were they in sunshine
By their firm-pawed mother,
Who marched them up the hill to home,
The woodchuck and his brother!

THE MYSTERIOUS CAT

Vachel Lindsay

I saw a proud, mysterious cat,
I saw a proud, mysterious cat
Too proud to catch a mouse or rat—
Mew, mew, mew.

But catnip she would eat, and purr,
But catnip she would eat, and purr,
And goldfish she did much prefer—
Mew, mew, mew.

I saw a cat—'twas but a dream,
I saw a cat—'twas but a dream
Who scorned the slave that brought her cream—
Mew, mew, mew.

Unless the slave were dressed in style,
Unless the slave were dressed in style
And knelt before her all the while—
Mew, mew, mew.

Did you ever hear of a thing like that?
Did you ever hear of a thing like that?
Did you ever hear of a thing like that?
Oh, what a proud mysterious cat.
Oh, what a proud mysterious cat.
Oh, what a proud mysterious cat.
Mew. . . mew. . . mew.

THE ANIMAL STORE
Rachel Field

If I had a hundred dollars to spend,
    Or maybe a little more,
I'd hurry as fast as my legs would go
    Straight to the animal store.

I wouldn't say, "How much for this or that?"
    "What kind of a dog is he?"
I'd buy as many as rolled an eye,
    Or wagged a tail at me!

I'd take the hound with the drooping ears
    That sits by himself alone;
Cockers and Cairns and wobbly pups
    For to be my very own.

I might buy a parrot all red and green
    And the monkey I saw before,
If I had a hundred dollars to spend,
    Or maybe a little more.

STEPHEN WANTS A MOUSE
Bertha Ten Eyck James

Mama, Daddy, will you bring me home a mouse?
I know we haven't room for many playmates in our house.
You told me that a puppy or a cat would be too much
And there's no use even thinking about elephants or such.
But a little gray mouse, with a little pink nose,
With little black eyes and quick little toes!
I could teach him how to roll a ball and play at hide and seek.
He'd run behind the table and whisper, "Sq-ueeky-eek."
And I'd say, "Peek!"
He could sit up very nicely on either of my knees
And I could teach him how to beg for crackers and for cheese.

Oh no, Stephen, you don't want mice!
They aren't so very pretty
And they aren't so very nice.
They're untidy in the house.

Mama, Daddy, *won't* you bring me home a mouse?

LITTLE WOODCHUCK'S FRIGHT
Etta F. Gilbert

Far above him, little woodchuck
Heard a grumbly, rumbly patter,
And he called, "Oh, Mother darling,
What can be the awful matter?

"Such a thump, thump, thump! It scares me.
Sounds to me like growly thunder.
Can it come down here and hurt us?
Now what can it be, I wonder?"

"What's that rumbling?" said his mother.
"It's just small boys in a hurry,
Running over our snug burrow.
We're quite safe down here. Don't worry."

99

SPRING PASTURES

Judy Van der Veer

I never saw such foolish cows
As my cows are today,
We turned them in the pasture,
They all began to play.

They galloped up the hillside,
Like horses running free,
They all cavorted down again
And shook their horns at me.

Their bells are ringing wildly
To celebrate the day,
The youngest calf and oldest cow
Think spring is here to stay!

SHARES

Judy Van der Veer

Of every field of grain I plant
The birds may have their share,
And mice and moles may have their bit,
For I shall never care.

Let rabbits come, and tell the squirrels
I will not point a gun;
For all the grain in all the world
I'd never spoil their fun.

I plant my fields on shares each year,
The sun and rain are free;
And all the hungry birds and beasts
May share alike with me.

SONG OF THE HERD

Judy Van der Veer

All day I followed
The wandering herd,
I knew every flower,
And loved every bird.

All the cattle grazed
Where the grass grew tall,
And I taught the calves
To answer my call.

And I made little songs
From the wind and the sky;
Not even the birds
Were as happy as I.

101

CHUMS

Arthur Guiterman

He sits and begs; he gives a paw;
   He is, as you can see,
The finest dog you ever saw
   And he belongs to me.

He follows everywhere I go
   And even when I swim.
I laugh because he thinks, you know,
   That I belong to him.

But still, no matter what we do,
   We never have a fuss,
And so I guess it must be true
   That *we* belong to *us*.

PET SHOW

Arthur Guiterman

We had a pet show out on our lawn,
And one little girl brought a real, live fawn,
And one small boy dragged a black bull calf,
And another had a coon that would make you laugh.
There were twelve nice dogs with well-groomed coats,
Twenty-two kittens with bows at their throats,
A turtle and a frog from Silver Lake,
A goldfish, a pony, and a garter snake,
Five red hens and four Plymouth Rocks,
And six tiny lizards in a cardboard box.
They were shown by children of various sizes
Who all had ice cream and all won prizes.

CAT

Mary Britton Miller

The black cat yawns
Opens her jaws,
Stretches her legs,
And shows her claws.

Then she gets up
And stands on four
Long stiff legs
And yawns some more.

She shows her sharp teeth,
She stretches her lip,
Her slice of a tongue
Turns up at the tip.

Lifting herself
On her delicate toes,
She arches her back
As high as it goes.

She lets herself down
With particular care,
And pads away
With her tail in the air.

103

OUR DONKEY
Tom Robinson

That's Nebuchadnezzar, our donkey, whose feet
Are planted so firmly out there in the street.
It's silly to pose with such obstinate pride
When you've nothing to show and nothing to hide.
But it must be pleasant when you've nothing to say
To throw back your head and let out a bray.

DOGS AND WEATHER
Winifred Welles

I'd like a different dog
  For every kind of weather—
A narrow greyhound for a fog,
  A wolfhound strange and white,
With a tail like a silver feather
  To run with in the night,
  When snow is still and winter stars are bright.

In the fall I'd like to see
  In answer to my whistle,
A golden spaniel look at me.
  But best of all for rain
A terrier, hairy as a thistle,
  To trot with fine disdain
  Beside me down the soaked, sweet-smelling lane.

HEROISM
Helen Wing

When I am as big as my father is now
  And wear a white collar to keep my chin up,
I won't be afraid any more of our cow
  Than I am of my own little bow-legged pup.

HORSES

Marchette Chute

I like a lot of people
   (Although it all depends),
But when it comes to horses
   I have some special friends.

There is a horse named Anna
   Who drove us through the Park.
I held the reins a minute;
   We stayed till nearly dark.

There is a horse named Peter
   Who brings us daffodils
And little pots of tulips
   To fill our window sills.

There is the pickle wagon
   And one that carries grapes.
They both have friendly horses
   Of different size and shapes.

I met a horse on Broadway,
   And what do you suppose?
He put his head down gently
   And loved me with his nose.

F. Eckart

MAUD-MISKA
PETERSHAM

THE MOCKINGBIRD

Maurice Lesemann

The mockingbird is the talkingest bird
That ever you'll meet in the month of May.
He teeters and tauters high in the tree,
And he talks all night and he talks all day.
He hardly ever has time to sing
Because of having so much to say.

Sometimes he's fussy and full of worry
(Oh much too busy to think of a song),
And then it's, "Hurry, now hurry, now hurry!
Ten-thirty, ten-thirty, ten-thirty, ten-thirty!"
Sometimes it's, "Hurry, now hurry, now hurry,
Now hurry, now hurry," the whole day long!

Sometimes he shouts in a rowdy tone:
"Hey, you, come here! Hey, you, come here!"
Sometimes he talks to himself alone:
"Chip-chip . . . chur-r, chur-r . . . chip-chip . . .
    chur-r, chur-r . . .
And ends with an odd little grating sound,
"Bz-z-z, bz-z-z!" like an ax on a grinding stone.

And then he'll call, "Potato, potato!"
(Now what is *that* for a bird to sing?)
And then he'll mix them all together:
"Hey, you, come here! Now hurry, now hurry,
Chip-chip, ten-thirty, potato, potato . . ."
And he teeters his tail and he twitches his wing . . .
"Chip-chip . . . chur-r, chur-r . . . bz-z, bz-z . . ."
A mockingbird is the *talkingest* thing!

A singer, too, as beautiful
As ever you'll hear in the month of May,
Carolling loud from the top of a tree . . .
But he talks all night and he talks all day.
He hardly ever has *time* to sing
Because of having so much to say!

THE SEA GULL
Elizabeth Coatsworth

A nautical bird the sea gull is
And a nautical bird is he.
He looks like a yacht when he floats on the waves
And faces into the sea.
When the sea gull flies, his wings
Are like pennons, narrow and white,
And the cry that the sea gull cries, is the gust
Of winds in the sails at night.
Oh, the sea gull has a rolling gait
(Like a sailor ashore!) on land,
And the footprints left by this nautical bird
Are like anchors drawn in the sand.

SONG OF GRANDFATHER THOMAS' PARROT
Elizabeth Coatsworth

Far off, far off
Those forests lie
Beneath a heavy
Molten sky.

Where I was born—
Oh, never more
At dusk shall I hear
Lions roar,

Nor see the monkeys
Leap and sway
From branch to branch
At dawn of day!

Behold me now,
Across the sea,
Watching mild ladies
Pour out tea!

108

HERON

Ella Young

His feet in water
See the white heron stand,
Swirl and shallow
Close at hand.
He eyes them sharply,
Keen angler is he:
His shadow lies
By the willow tree.
Ye fishes all,
Both great and small,
Take note of his shadow
And flee!

SCHOOL FOR SANDPIPERS

Elizabeth Honness

The small sandpipers go to school
Upon the sandy shore;
The ocean is their teacher,
She has a fearful roar.

She shows them how to catch the crabs
That burrow on the beach,
How to run behind a wave,
Then soar above its reach.

They do their featherstitching
In rows along the sand,
Until the sea erases it
With foam upon her hand.

The grown-up terns and elder gulls,
Who scorn their childish fun,
Drop clamshells down to break it up
And see sandpipers run!

FAWN'S FIRST JOURNEY
Maud E. Uschold

Softly comes the wary doe
When the night is fringed with dawn,
Where the hushed waters flow;
Like her shadow moves her fawn.

Sampling morning winds for signs,
Starting at each woodland sound;
Soft as needles from the pines,
Tiny hooves fall on the ground.

Softly steps the dappled fawn
Close beside the watchful doe
In the silence of the dawn,
Where the shadowed waters flow.

SONG FOR WARREN
(Who Loves Wild Animals)
Adele Jordan Tarr

Down in the foothills of Tennessee
    The train had stopped, and I sat inside:
And I saw, in the top of a tall, bare tree
    A baby raccoon with a fuzzy hide.
I looked at him, and he looked at me
    With his bright black eyes, and he seemed to say,
"Now don't you wish you were free, like me,
    Instead of shut in a cage, all day?"

THE FROG
Marion K. Seavey

The frog in the water has goggly eyes
And a mouth that is much too wide,
But I wouldn't think of telling him so—
For even a frog has pride!

110

MY DOG

Tom Robinson

My dog listens when I talk.
He goes with me for a walk.
When I sleep, he's sleepy too.
He does everything I do.
He has eyes that always show
He knows everything I know.
I never do a thing but he
Thinks it is all right for me.
When I speak, he always minds.
He shares with me things he finds.
When other people say I'm bad,
He hangs his head and looks so sad.
He cuddles up and laps my hand
And tells me he can understand.

THE BROWN BEAR

Mary Austin

Now the wild bees that hive in the rocks
Are winding their horns, elfin shrill,
And hark, at the pine tree the woodpecker knocks,
And the speckled grouse pipes on the hill.
Now the adder's dull brood wakes to run,
Now the sap mounts abundant and good,
And the brown bear has turned with his side to the sun
In his lair in the depth of the wood—
Old Honey-Paw wakes in the wood.

"Oh, a little more slumber," says he,
"And a little more turning to sleep,"
But he feels the spring fervor that hurries the bee
And the hunger that makes the trout leap;
So he ambles by thicket and trail,
So he noses the tender young shoots,
In the spring of the year at the sign of the quail
The brown bear goes digging for roots—
For sappy and succulent roots.

Oh, as still goes the wolf on his quest
As the spotted snake glides through the rocks,
And the deer and the sheep count the lightest foot best,
And slinking and sly trots the fox.
But fleet-foot and light-foot will stay,
And fawns by their mothers will quail
At the saplings that snap and the thickets that sway
When Honey-Paw takes to the trail—
When he shuffles and grunts on the trail.

He has gathered the ground squirrel's hoard,
He has rifled the store of the bees,
He has caught the young trout at the shoals of the ford
And stripped the wild plums from the trees;
So robbing and raging he goes,
And the right to his pillage makes good
Till he rounds out the year at the first of the snows
In his lair in the depths of the wood—
Old Honey-Paw sleeps in the wood.

THE SQUIRREL

Mildred Bowers Armstrong

He wore a question mark for tail,
An overcoat of gray,
He sat up straight to eat a nut.
He liked to tease and play,
And if we ran around his tree,
He went the other way.

THE CRICKET
Marjorie Barrows

And when the rain had gone away
    And it was shining everywhere,
I ran out on the walk to play
    And found a little bug was there.

And he was running just as fast
    As any little bug could run,
Until he stopped for breath at last,
    All black and shiny in the sun.

And then he chirped a song to me
    And gave his wings a little tug,
And *that's* the way he showed that he
    Was very glad to be a bug!

LITTLE FOLKS IN THE GRASS*
Annette Wynne

In the grass
A thousand little people pass,
And all about myriad little eyes look out,
For there are houses on every side
Where the little folks abide,
Where the little folks take tea
On a grass blade near a tree;
Where they hold their Sabbath meetings,
Pass each other, giving greetings.
So remember when you pass
Through the grass;
Little folks are everywhere;
Walk quite softly, take great care
Lest you hurt them unaware,
Lest the giant that is YOU
Pull a house down with his shoe,
Pull a house down, roof and all,
Killing children, great and small;
So the wee eyes look at you
As you walk the meadows through;
So remember when you pass
Through the grass.

*Reprinted by permission of the publishers, J. B. Lippincott Company, from *For Days and Days*, by Annette Wynne. Copyright, 1919, by J. B. Lippincott Company.

SMALL HOMES

Carl Sandburg

The green bug sleeps in the white lily ear.
The red bug sleeps in the white magnolia.
Shiny wings, you are choosers of color.
You have taken your summer bungalows wisely.

THE LIZARD

Ann Chalmers

The lizard is a wizard
At playing hide and seek.
He darts among the cactuses
With a lightning streak.

He sits upon a flat rock
Quiet as a stick,
Then suddenly he's off again
With a long-tailed flick.

Down across the river bed
Around a yucca tree
He stopped, but only long enough,
Perhaps, to count to three.

Then in and out the chaparral
Across the desert sand,
He won the game and disappeared
In wizard-lizard land.

OUR BURRO

Clara E. Randall

In our high-up mountain town
We rode a burro up and down.
We rode him to the country store
Where we got boxes, three or four;
Then on each side we made a pack
And got on him and rode him back.
We did this quite a while until
He just sat down and let us spill.

115

PENGUIN SUMMER
Kathryn Worth

In cold Antarctic Ocean
Where penguins watch the summer,
No coast is live with yellow bloom
Or song of yellow-hummer.

No fields are bright with clover:
The only grass they know
Is emerald-colored pack ice
And beds of frozen snow.

Instead of singing thrushes
Piercing delightful weather,
They hear the voice of icebergs
Muttering together.

THE POLITE PENGUINS
Adelaide Love

Penguins are very polite, you know.
They live where it's usually forty below
And there's nothing but wind and ice and snow.
But the penguins are very polite.

Whenever a vessel comes to explore
The land that few people have seen before,
The penguins all rush down to the shore.
Oh, the penguins are very polite!

In the black and white suits they always wear,
They stand with a dignified elegant air
And welcome the men with a friendly stare.
The penguins are very polite.

If they could, they would all say: "How do you do?"
And: "How does this climate agree with you?"
Or: "The sun will rise in a month or two."
Oh, the penguins are very polite!

116

SEASHORE GOSSIP

J. Lilian Vandevere

The waves told the gull,
   And the gray gull listened.
The gull told the sand,
   And the wet sand glistened.
The sand told a sandpiper,
   He said, "Peep!
What a splendid secret—
   Too good to keep."
So he told a rock,
   And the rock said, "Never!"
The rock told a shell,
   And the shell said, "Clever!"
A fat little crab answered,
   "Good for him!"
Did you hear the secret?
   John learned to swim!

WHALE

Geoffrey Dearmer

Wouldn't you like to be a whale
   And sail serenely by—
An eighty-foot whale from your tip to your tail
   And a tiny, briny eye?
Wouldn't you like to wallow
   Where nobody says "Come out!"?
Wouldn't you *love* to swallow
   And blow all the brine about?
Wouldn't you like to be always clean
But never have to wash, I mean,
   And wouldn't you love to spout—
     O yes, just think—
A feather of spray as you sail away,
And rise and sink and rise and sink,
   And blow all the brine about?

THE HORNBILL FAMILY
Carl S. Junge

The hollow of a jungle tree
Is where the Hornbills choose to nest,
And there the mother that's to be
Awaits the day when she'll be blest.
She's laid her egg and stay she will,
Until she's hatched out little Bill.

Now Mr. Hornbill does his bit,
With gobs of clay he seals her in,
Just leaving a small narrow slit
Through which to feed his kith and kin.
"No wife of mine," says he, "shall roam.
A woman's place is in the home!"

But in good time, she is set free,
And with her comes out Junior, too.
Dad looks him over, then says he—
"He does, it seems, take after you,
And too he looks like me; but still,
I think my dear, he has your bill!"

mister mckee

A STRANGE BEAST

Carl S. Junge

The Malay Tapir it is claimed
Is most appropriately named.
Yet stranger than its tapered shape
Is what at first seems like a cape
Of white upon a blackish hide
Draped on its back and down each side.
When this strange coat we now compare
To coats the junior tapirs wear
It's rather tame, since these young tots
Wear coats made up of stripes and spots.

THE DINOSAUR

Carl S. Junge

The Dinosaur,
A beast of yore,
Doesn't live here
Any more.

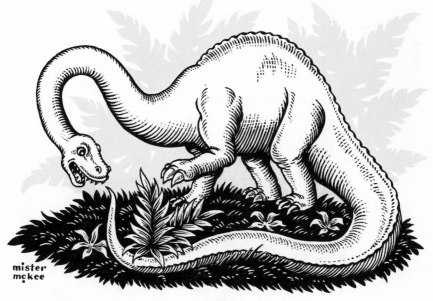

119

MY DOG

James S. Tippett

I do not love my dog because—
He's good at doing tricks
Like standing on his two hind feet
Or fetching balls and sticks.

I do not love my dog because—
He's gentle and polite
And barks to drive away the things
That prowl around at night.

I do not love my dog because—
He really is quite fine.
But oh, I love my dog because
I'm his and he is mine!

GRATITUDE

Marie Louise Scott

I know a shaggy little dog
As poor as poor can be,
Who comes each day to my back door,
And begs imploringly.

And I make haste to get a bone
And also scraps of meat,
Or any other kind of food
That he might like to eat.

And, though he cannot speak a word,
I know he will not fail
To say "I love you" with his eyes
And "Thank you" with his tail.

Cecile Benedard, 49

A KITTEN*

Eleanor Farjeon

He's nothing much but fur
And two round eyes of blue,
He has a giant purr
And a midget mew.
He darts and pats the air,
He starts and cocks his ear,
When there is nothing there
For him to see and hear.
He runs around in rings,
But why we cannot tell;
With sideways leaps he springs
At things invisible—
Then half-way through a leap
His startled eyeballs close,
And he drops off to sleep
With one paw on his nose.

*Reprinted by permission of the publishers, J. B. Lippincott Company, from *Eleanor Farjeon's Poems for Children.* Copyright, 1951, by Eleanor Farjeon.

A DOG

Aileen Fisher

If you didn't have a dog
('Cause everyone *should*)
And you knew they were fun,
Then of course you *would*.

If you DON'T have a dog
(Or at least until)
Keep asking after one,
Then, of course, you *will*.

I have a dog . . .
And he's black as night.
But you can have one,
If you *want*, that's white.

Or you can have one
That's as brown as wood,
But you *ought* to have a dog
('Cause everyone *should*).

MIRANDA

Frances Barbara Grafe

Miranda, my kitten,
Is cute as can be.
She gets up but she can't
Get down from a tree.

When she sees a fly she
Will jump into space.
For all that she knows
She will land on her face.

She chases her tail all
Round the veranda,
Not knowing, of course, it
Belongs to Miranda!

123

THE HOPPITY TOAD

Ruth Stephens Porter

I like the funny
Old hoppity toad.
He opens his eyes,
Watching for flies,
Winking,
Blinking,
Always thinking,
It's fun to
Hop over
The road!

THE LUCKY SNAIL

Winifred Welles

The snail's a lucky fellow, he can go
　　The whole world over if he chooses,
Through blazing suns, or where the white flakes blow,
　　Yet his own home he never loses.
　　　　He can behold what's strange and beautiful,
　　　　While still remaining very comfortable.

He goes afar yet never is away,
　　Whose house rests always on his shoulder—
He dreams beneath a fern's soft spray,
　　Or dares to climb the hardest boulder.
　　　　He can be cozy and yet love to roam,
　　　　A traveler who always is at home.

THE BUG AND BEETLE CIRCUS

Carolyn Forsyth

I saw a silly circus
In a windwood where I went,
A Bug And Beetle Circus
Beneath a burdock tent,
(An open tent, I should explain,
Not much protection in a rain.)

124

A spider walked a tightrope there
And did not trip or fall.
She even kept her balance well
Without a parasol.
The very smallest insects
Were hanging by their knees
Or swinging upside down upon
A little twig trapeze.
The mumbling, bumbling June bug
Was always falling down.
He waved his hands and kicked his feet
Just like a circus clown.
The caterpillar moved about
Like any well-trained seal.
She did a kind of wriggly dance
Without a toe or heel.
Oh, everything was going fine
Until the rain came down!
Then all the actors ran and hid
So none of them would drown.

SONG FOR A COUNTRY NIGHT
Elizabeth-Ellen Long

Night is not still, who thinks it so
Has never heard the come and go
Of wind in leaves, the sound of grass
Parting to let small creatures pass,
Has never lain awake alone
And listened to the baritone
Of frogs in hidden ponds, with thin
Cricket sopranos joining in.

Night is not still, who tries to say
It is, has missed the moths that stray
Abroad by dark to tap in vain
At every lighted windowpane,
Has let go by the velvet flight
Of owls in air lanes out of sight,
And failed to chart by their shrill cries
The course of bats through starry skies.

FARMERS

William Alexander Percy

I watch the farmers in their fields
And marvel secretly.
They are so very calm and sure,
They have such dignity . . . .

Their pleasure is so grave and full
When gathered crops are trim,
You know they think their work was done
In partnership with Him.

THE CHRISTMAS CALF

Judy Van der Veer

The cows are milked, the horses fed;
And nestled in the sweet warm hay,
There sleeps a little spotted calf
Born early on this Christmas day.
I found it when I came to milk,
Before the stars had left the sky;
Its mother standing over it,
With deep and watchful eye.
And though the wind outside was cold,
The big barn was a kindly place;
I moved my lantern back and forth
And saw it light each creature's face.
I pitched down hay and thought how good
And sweet a place a barn may be;
I heard the pigeons move about
On rafters where I could not see.
The barn was filled with sound of wings
As pigeons wakened into flight;
And then I thought of Angel wings
Above a barn one Holy Night . . .
Of barn made sacred by a Child
Who came to bless all helpless things—
(The little spotted calf slept on,
All unaware of shining wings.)

PUPPIES

Marguerite Gode

Puppies are squirmy
And wiggly and cuddly,
And when it rains
Their feet are mud puddly.
They strew things
And chew things
In puppy dog prankings
And waggle their way
Out of scoldings and spankings.

THE CREATURE BRONTOSAURUS
Dorothy Aldis

Over a hundred million
Centuries ago
Before the Rocky Mountains
Raised their heads of snow,
Making hard and nubbly
A land that once was swamps,
The creature Brontosaurus
Went on his ponderous romps.

His name means Thunder Reptile
But he couldn't make a sound
As over eighty feet of him
Went slithering around;
Poor fellow—how upsetting
It must have been to not
Be able to express himself
When sleepy, cross, or hot.

Forty tons of temper
Without a single whimp
You'd think would leave him feeling
A little long and limp.
But he just stamped the harder
Upon the sandy ground
And made those giant footsteps
That scientists have found.

Even today we see them
Planted on old stones,
Even today they keep on finding
Brontosaurus bones
Which people in museums
Fit together till

The ancient age old creature
Rears up—bleak and still.

In all his mighty body
His brain weighed just one pound.
So maybe we're not missing much
Not having him around.
Perhaps his heart was big though—
Perhaps he shed a tear
For lack of laps to climb into
Or scratchings on the ear.

THE DINOSAUR

Clara E. Randall

We were looking at the book
About a dinosaur;
But we never found the place
That told what he was for.

THE KANGAROO

Elizabeth Coatsworth

It is a curious thing that you
don't wish to be a kangaroo,
  to hop hop hop
  and never stop
the whole day long and the whole night, too!

To hop across Australian plains
with tails that sweep behind like trains
  and small front paws
  and pointed jaws
and pale neat coats to shed the rains.

If skies be blue, if skies be gray,
they bound in the same graceful way
  into dim space
  at such a pace
that where they go there's none to say!

DINNER HORSES*
Lucy Sprague Mitchell

The horse of the plains sleeps out in the rains;
The farm horse comes home to a stall.
One end for his tail, one end for his head,
He sleeps in his dining room, eats in his bed,
Without ever minding at all.

COALIE
Janet Norris Bangs

Coalie rules stables and feeding lot
    And he is the pet of the pasture, too;
He is gleaming black with a white star spot,
    His tiny hoofs run swift and true.

I ride—it is Coalie who sets the speed,
    His mane all grass-tied to make it curl,
I call him my wonderful galloping steed
    And I guess he thinks I'm a tomboy girl.

It is like flying through the air!
    We own the cornfields, sky, and space,
We brush wild blossoms into my hair,
    The prairie wind blows into my face.

He winnows a path from the goldenrod,
    Pony mouth full of clover that tickles his eyes,
And he darts through the dew of the meadow sod
    Frisking his tail at the dragonflies.

We know every road from town to town,
    And Coalie will linger where grass grows deep,
But he heads for home when the sun goes down
    With one quick dash for supper and sleep.

The clover never smells half so sweet,
    And I'm never so near to the birds in the lane,
As when I ride Coalie's galloping feet,
    Bareback, and holding his grass-tied mane.

*Taken from *Here and Now Story Book*, by Lucy Sprague Mitchell, published and copyright, 1921, by E. P. Dutton & Co., Inc., New York.

THE RUNAWAY

Robert Frost

Once when the snow of the year was beginning to fall,
We stopped by a mountain pasture to say "Whose colt?"
A little Morgan had one forefoot on the wall,
The other curled at his breast. He dipped his head
And snorted at us. And then he had to bolt.
We heard the miniature thunder where he fled
And we saw him, or thought we saw him, dim and gray,
Like a shadow against the curtain of falling flakes.
"I think the little fellow's afraid of the snow.
He isn't winter-broken. It isn't play
With the little fellow at all. He's running away.
I doubt if even his mother could tell him, 'Sakes,
It's only weather.' He'd think she didn't know!
Where is his mother? He can't be out alone."
And now he comes again with a clatter of stone,
And mounts the wall again with whited eyes
And all his tail that isn't hair up straight.
He shudders his coat as if to throw off flies.
"Whoever it is that leaves him out so late,
When other creatures have gone to stall and bin,
Ought to be told to come and take him in."

131

FROGS

Helen Wing

The papa bullfrog has a voice
    That's very loud and deep,
The baby frogs have voices that
    Can only make a peep,
And every night I hear them talk
    Before I go to sleep.

BOOZER*

Lysbeth Boyd Borie

Boozer,
He
Is my dog.
He
Never
Runs away;
He's an
Old black
Setter
And he
Sets
All
Day.

THE CAMEL

Clara E. Randall

For centuries in desert lands
The camel tramped the burning sands;
No other brute could stand the heat,
No other had well-padded feet.
But now he doesn't travel far.
The Arabs use a motor car.

*Reprinted by permission of the publishers, J. B. Lippincott Company, from *Poems for Peter*, by Lysbeth Boyd Borie. Copyright, 1928, by J. B. Lippincott Company.

132

FAMILIAR FRIENDS

James S. Tippett

The horses, the pigs,
And the chickens,
The turkeys, the ducks,
And the sheep!
I can see all my friends
From my window
As soon as I waken
From sleep.

The cat on the fence
Is out walking.
The geese have gone down
For a swim.
The pony comes trotting
Right up to the gate;
He knows I have candy
For him.

The cows in the pasture
Are switching
Their tails to keep off
The flies.
And the old mother dog
Has come out in the yard
With five pups to give me
A surprise.

RAINY DAY

Bee Bowers

Three little ducks walk out in the rain.
    Quack! Quack! Quack!
Each with his waterproof feathers
    Folded along his back,
Each with his little pink rubbers
    Waddles along in to town.
Each finds a pond of which he is fond
    And stands in it upside down!

133

THE BIRD'S NEST
John Drinkwater

I know a place in the ivy on a tree,
Where a bird's nest is, and the eggs are three
And the bird is brown, and the eggs are blue,
And the twigs are old, but the moss is new,
And I go quite near, though I think I should have heard
The sound of me watching if I had been a bird.

THE MUSICAL MICE
Frances Frost

The wood mouse and his wife
who came to live with me
were curious about
my husky minstrelsy.

When I burst forth in song—
if you could call it that—
they'd peer down from their beam,
big-eared, bright-eyed, and fat,

and squeak accompaniment.
Mouse-musically inclined,
they liked the sounds and crumbs
produced by humankind.

And I was overwhelmed
at such an audience
conducting with their tails
The Pirates of Penzance!

134

ADOLFUSS

Fredrika Shumway Smith

Adolfuss was a scornful cat
Who felt so big and proud
That when he walked he stretched himself.
His mew was very loud.

When other cats invited him
To join them in their play
Adolfuss just looked *scornful!*
And slowly walked away.

LITTLE CATS

Marguerite Gode

Little cats
With stand-up tails
Are like small ships
With brave new sails,
And when their hind feet
Travel faster
They tail spin
Into disaster.

CHANT OF THE CHIPMUNK

Arthur Guiterman

Chipmunk, chipmunk, chip, chip, chip,
Bright eyes, black stripes, quick as a whip;
Cling and swing where the alders dip,
Chipmunk, chipmunk, chip, chip, chip.

Chipmunk, chipmunk, chip, chip, chip,
Gay little rascal, pert little rip.
Over boulders you lightly skip,
Chipmunk, chipmunk, chip, chip, chip.

135

THE PASTURE
Robert Frost

I'm going out to clean the pasture spring;
I'll only stop to rake the leaves away
(And wait to watch the water clear, I may):
I shan't be gone long.—You come too.

I'm going out to fetch the little calf
That's standing by the mother. It's so young,
It totters when she licks it with her tongue.
I shan't be gone long.—You come too.

I STARE AT THE COW
Polly Chase

I stare at the cow
And
The cow stares at me.
I do not bow.
It would start a row
To bow
To a cow!
I think it is safer to let her be,
Munching and crunching
S-O S-L--E---E--P--I--L-Y.
But look at her now!
What a different cow!
She's beginning to bow!

So I RUN for a tree!

THE HOUSE CAT*
Annette Wynne

The house cat sits
And smiles and sings.
He knows a lot
Of secret things.

*Reprinted by permission of the publishers, J. B. Lippincott Company, from *For Days and Days*, by Annette Wynne. Copyright, 1919, by J. B. Lippincott Company.

MODEL FOR ME

Tom Robinson

Beulah's our cow; she drinks her fill,
  Then quiet as a snail,
Lies in the shade and chews her cud,
  And keeps time with her tail.

But she has no one to scold or nag,
  And I could keep quiet too,
If I just had a tail to wag
  And had a cud to chew.

RABBIT TRACKS
Aileen Fisher

There's a crevice in the granite
  in the mountains where I live.
There's a rabbit in a burrow
  in the rocks, I'm positive.
Or maybe there are several
  hidden down between the cracks,
But all that ever shows of them
    are tracks
        and tracks
            and
                tracks.

There's a snowdrift on the granite
  in the mountains where I stay,
But underneath in burrows
  it is warm and tucked away.
And though my puppy scratches
  and we peer in all the cracks,
The rabbits only let us see
    their tracks
        and tracks
            and
                tracks.

THE HOUSE OF THE MOUSE
Lucy Sprague Mitchell

The house of the mouse
is a wee little house,
a green little house in the grass,
which big clumsy folk
may hunt and may poke
and still never see as they pass
this sweet little, neat little,
wee little, green little,
cuddle-down hide-away
house in the grass.

138

FIELD MOUSE

Emilie Fendall Johnson

A field mouse passed our house today
And we persuaded him to stay.
We gave him water and some food,
Some crackers that he chewed and chewed.
We made a box of cardboard firm,
Where he could run and play and squirm.
And then we made the softest pillow,
Of moss and grass and pussywillow.
A mouse has seldom had such care,
But later on he wasn't there.
We looked and looked and looked all day,
But our field mouse had run away.
We were so very, very sad;
He was the only mouse we had!

NIGHT PRAYER FOR WILD THINGS

Elizabeth-Ellen Long

Lord, in thy loving-kindness keep
All little things which lie asleep
In nest or burrow out of sight,
Please keep them safe throughout the night.

The fledgling bird who takes his rest
Beneath his mother's soft warm breast,
The baby rabbit and the fawn,
Please, let them live to see the dawn.

Lord, in thy gentle mercy spare
All small things sleeping everywhere
In leafy hammock overhead
Or some grass-hidden trundle bed.

The young squirrel in his windy house,
The new-born chipmunk and the mouse,
From cricket call to song of lark,
Dear Lord, be with them in the dark!

139

EASTER IN THE WOODS
Frances Frost

This dawn when the mountain cherry lifts
its frail white bloom among dark pines,
and chipmunks flash small happy paws
along old tumbled boundary lines,
this golden morning when the vixen
nuzzles her five young foxes forth
to roll in ferns in the Easter sun,—
again the woods know soft green birth.

Snuffed by a puffball infant rabbit
are yellow violets by the spring;
among half-opened apple buds
a wood thrush tilts his head to sing.
Risen is He! And they are His,
who scamper under warm blue skies,
who nibble little fists of grass,
and gaze on earth with shy glad eyes.

141

Part IV:

HERE COME THE FAIRIES

OFFER

Mildred Bowers Armstrong

Come around at seven
When the moon is out;
I'll ask the queen to send a guide
To show us both about.

142

You'd better bring your overshoes
And a cover for your hair;
You'll soon be wet with night dew,
And burrs are everywhere.

You must watch sharply
And not cough or sneeze;
You will see the lanterns
Of stars among the trees.

You must listen closely
And not draw away;
You'll hear the misty fairies
Laughing in their play.

THE ROAD TO RAFFYDIDDLE

Mildred Plew Meigs

On the road to Raffydiddle
Sits a fiddler with a fiddle
  And there beneath the
    melting of the moon,
Each night he puts his chin
To his cheery violin
  And plucks him out
    a frisky feather tune.

And when as they go down
To Raffydiddle town
  The people hear him
    playing in the dusk,
Beside the crooked stile
They pause a little while
  To dance beneath the moon
    the moneymusk.

Oh, the fiddler he is slight
And his hair is salty white,
  And none who live
    will ever know his name.
But when he sets his bow
A tickle to and fro
  Each foot begins to
    flicker like a flame.

Oh, it's fun to see them come
When they hear the fiddle strum,
   All the lords and all the ladies
      with their cooks;
All the butchers and the bakers,
All the cake and candymakers,
   All the scholars with their noses
      in their books.

With their breeches in a crease,
Come the gorgeous blue police,
   Come the cowboys
      with their chaps upon their shins,
Comes a tailor spick-and-span
And a scissor-grinder man
   And a seamstress with
      her bosom full of pins.

Oh, it's fun to see them prance
At the Raffydiddle dance,
   All the doctors and
      the judges in their gowns,
All the farmers in their slickers,
All the rag and bottle pickers,
   All the gypsies and the jockeys
      and the clowns.

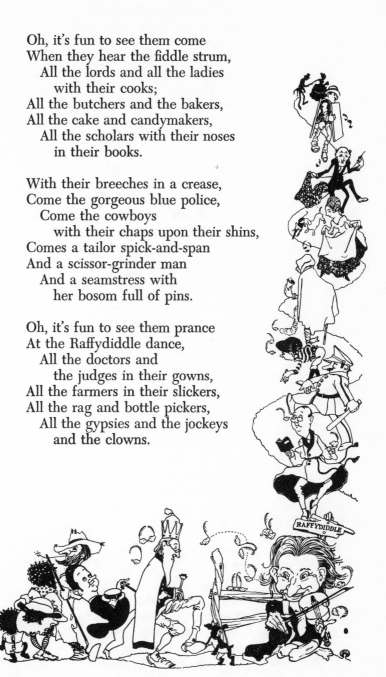

There below the blinky stars
Come the tinkers and the tars,
    And the brigands with their
        daggers and their dirks,
Come the vixens and the villains
And the mammies with their "chilluns"
    And the chauffeurs and the
        soda water clerks.

On the road to Raffydiddle
Sits a fiddler with a fiddle,
    And round about the fiddler
        falls a cloak;
While past the crooked stile
In Raffydiddle file
    Come flitting all the
        merrymaking folk.

Oh, the fiddler he is old,
He is eery to behold,
    And none have guessed
        the riddle of his race;
But folk who linger long
To hear his final song
    Have often seen a sadness
        in his face.

On the road to Raffydiddle,
Sits a fiddler with a fiddle,
    And he fiddles and he fiddles
        in the dusk,
But those who come at dawn
Will find the fiddler gone
    And all the music melted
        into musk.

Every Raffydiddle tune
Will be shut up in the moon
    And none who seek will find
        his dark abode,
But where the music thinned
A creepy little wind
    Will ripple down
        the Raffydiddle road.

THE SECOND–HAND SHOP

Rowena Bennett

Down in the grasses
Where the grasshoppers hop
And the katydids quarrel
And the flutter-moths flop—
Down in the grasses
Where the beetle goes "plop"
An old withered fairy
Keeps a second-hand shop.

She sells lost thimbles
For fairy milk pails
And burnt-out matches
For fence posts and rails.
She sells stray marbles
To bowl on the green,
And bright scattered beads
For the crown of the queen.

Oh don't feel badly
Over things that you lose
Like spin tops or whistles
Or dolls' buckled shoes;
They may be things that
Fairy folks can use;
For down in the grasses
Where the grasshoppers hop
A withered old fairy
Keeps a second-hand shop.

THE ELF AND THE DORMOUSE

Oliver Herford

Under a toadstool
   Crept a wee Elf,
Out of the rain
   To shelter himself.

Under the toadstool,
   Sound asleep,
Sat a big Dormouse
   All in a heap.

Trembled the wee Elf,
   Frightened, and yet
Fearing to fly away
   Lest he get wet.

To the next shelter—
   Maybe a mile!
Sudden the wee Elf
   Smiled a wee smile,

Tugged till the toadstool
   Toppled in two.
Holding it over him
   Gaily he flew.

Soon he was safe home
   Dry as could be.
Soon woke the Dormouse—
   "Good gracious me!

Where is my toadstool?"
   Loud he lamented.
—And that 's how umbrellas
   First were invented.

PLEASE

Rose Fyleman

Please be careful where you tread,
   The fairies are about;
Last night when I had gone to bed,
   I heard them creeping out.
And wouldn't it be a dreadful thing
   To do a fairy harm?
To crush a little delicate wing
   Or bruise a tiny arm?
They're all about the place, I know,
   So do be careful where you go.

BOREDOM

Mildred Bowers Armstrong

I can't blow bubbles,
I haven't any pipe.
I can't eat apples,
They haven't turned ripe.
If I sit quiet for an hour or two,
Will the Fairy Queen come
   to tell me what to do?

CONSOLATION

Rose Fyleman

You may be very ugly and freckledy and small
   And have a little stubby nose that's not a nose at all;
You may be bad at spelling and you may be worse at sums,
   You may have stupid fingers that your Nanna says are thumbs,
And lots of things you look for you may never, never find,
   But if you love the fairies—you don't mind.

You may be rather frightened when you read of wolves and bears
   Or when you pass the cupboard-place beneath the attic stairs;
You may not always like it when thunder makes a noise
   That seems so much, much bigger than little girls and boys;
You may feel rather lonely when you waken in the night,
   But if the fairies love you—it's all right.

149

DEEP SEA SONG

Marjorie Barrows

I'd like to sail
On a baby whale;
  I'd take my horn
And I'd take my pail,
And through green waves
  We'd splash right down
Past coral caves
  Of Mermaid Town.

I'd play a tune
All afternoon
  To a rainbow fish
And a coral moon,
And a seashell wing
  And anemone.
Then p'r'aps I'd bring
  Them back with me.

Then home we'd sail
  And sail
    And sail,
And I would thank my baby whale,
Who'd say, "You're welcome!"
    With his tail.

150

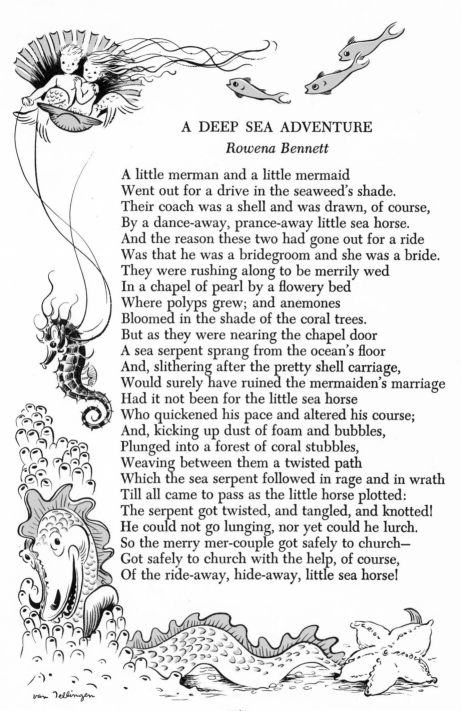

A DEEP SEA ADVENTURE

Rowena Bennett

A little merman and a little mermaid
Went out for a drive in the seaweed's shade.
Their coach was a shell and was drawn, of course,
By a dance-away, prance-away little sea horse.
And the reason these two had gone out for a ride
Was that he was a bridegroom and she was a bride.
They were rushing along to be merrily wed
In a chapel of pearl by a flowery bed
Where polyps grew; and anemones
Bloomed in the shade of the coral trees.
But as they were nearing the chapel door
A sea serpent sprang from the ocean's floor
And, slithering after the pretty shell carriage,
Would surely have ruined the mermaiden's marriage
Had it not been for the little sea horse
Who quickened his pace and altered his course;
And, kicking up dust of foam and bubbles,
Plunged into a forest of coral stubbles,
Weaving between them a twisted path
Which the sea serpent followed in rage and in wrath
Till all came to pass as the little horse plotted:
The serpent got twisted, and tangled, and knotted!
He could not go lunging, nor yet could he lurch.
So the merry mer-couple got safely to church—
Got safely to church with the help, of course,
Of the ride-away, hide-away, little sea horse!

151

THE DRYAD

Rowena Bennett

A dryad lives inside this tree,
  I'm sure it must be so
For I can hear her whispering
  When summer breezes blow;
And I can see her flowing hair
  Flash green-gold in the sun
As she nods to all the shadowy things
  That hug her feet or run
Along the edges of the wind.
At night her leafy locks are pinned
With silver stars, and on her wrist
She wears the new moon in a twist.

I WISH I LIVED IN ELFLAND

Anne Pérez-Guerra

I wish I lived in Elfland,
  Where the sky is colored rose
Above the fields and woodlands,
  And a cold wind never blows.

Where it only rains on Fridays
  And the drops splash into jewels,
Where brownies hide in hedges
  And turn wise men to fools,

With bucketsful of nickels
  For every child to share.
I wish I lived in Elfland.
  I'd be a giant there!

152

I KEEP THREE WISHES READY*

Annette Wynne

I keep three wishes ready,
Lest I should chance to meet,
Any day a fairy
Coming down the street.

I'd hate to have to stammer,
Or have to think them out,
For it's very hard to think things up
When a fairy is about.

And I'd hate to lose my wishes,
For fairies fly away,
And perhaps I'd never have a chance
On any other day.

So I keep three wishes ready,
Lest I should chance to meet,
Any day a fairy
Coming down the street.

*Reprinted by permission of the publishers, J. B. Lippincott Company, from *For Days and Days*, by Annette Wynne. Copyright, 1919, by J. B. Lippincott Company.

FAERY RIDERS
Ella Young

When the moon is round and white
The Faery Riders shake the night
With song and laughter going by:
I love to hear the noise they make,
The pine trees hear it too, and wake;
It fills the room in which I lie.

I hear the trumpets long and loud,
I hear the voices of a crowd,
I hear the horses prancing by:
All night they pass, and pass, and pass,
But not one little blade of grass
Is trampled down or turned awry.

If I could see their faces plain,
Or run beside the bridle rein
Of Mab the Queen, as she comes by:
I might know all the Faeries know,
And follow, follow where they go
Before the sun climbs up the sky.

But though I hurry might and main
To look out through the windowpane,
I never see them passing by.
Just when I reach the window sill
The music stops and all is still:
Only the wind is passing by.

FAIRY AND I

Marjorie Allen Anderson

We planted both our gardens,
My fairy friend and I;
I didn't really see her,
But I knew she was close by.

I hoed and raked my garden,
And made it soft and new;
While near me in the bushes,
I could hear her working too.

And now our little gardens
Have suddenly sprung up;
In mine are tiny carrots,
And in hers—a buttercup!

THE GARDEN HAT SHOP
Rowena Bennett

A meadow mouse with a long tail on it
Went out to shop for an Easter bonnet.
The shop of Madam Mole she chose
Because it advertised: "CHAPEAUX,
IN EVERY COLOR FROM BLUE
    TO ROSE."

She tried a bluebell on for size
But found it did not suit her eyes.
She tried a crocus on for shape
But saw it did not match her cape.

She said, "I do not want a quill,
They're much too stiff. Have you a frill?"
The madam brought a daffodil
With little golden ruffles on it.
"Oh what a lovely Easter bonnet!"
Exclaimed the mouse, "It's just the thing
To make me feel in style this spring."

She paid the mole a moneywort
And went off looking pleased
    and pert.

PARADE OF THE ANIMAL CRACKERS
Rowena Bennett

The animal crackers all lived on a table.
They hadn't a cage. They hadn't a stable;
But they liked to parade as best they were able.
(They liked to parade
With the help and the aid
    Of Tommy and Mabel.)

The animal crackers all walked in a troop.
They tried not to fall into red seas of soup.
But they slid from a spoon-bridge right into a cup
And two greedy giants soon gobbled them up.

157

QUESTIONS

Laura Lee Randall

Butterfly, butterfly, light as summer air,
Darting up, floating down, drifting everywhere;
    Are the fairies using you
    As airplane for a fairy crew?

Firefly, firefly, little living spark,
Gleaming high, shining low, flashing through the dark,
    Did the fairies send for you
    To lead them home through dusk and dew?

TEDDY BEAR DANCE

Ruth Dixon

Teddy bears are dancing
    Hip—hip—hop!
Merrily they're prancing
    Flip—flip—flop!
Now they stumble
Now they fumble
Now they tumble
In a jumble—
    Hippety—
        (They're up again)—
        Hop!

OVER THE CHIMNEY-TOPS

Rowena Bennett

Over the chimney-tops Huffen Puff goes—
He is the one who is light on his toes,
He is the one with a smoke-beard that curls
Round him and round him whenever he twirls.
A beard that's as gray and as white as the snows
Huffen Puff grows when he walks on his toes
Over the chimney-tops at the day's close.

Out of the chimney-top Huffen Puff comes
Pulling himself up with smudgy gray thumbs—
Thick as a dwarf in a muffler and cape
Up he comes, up he comes, changing his shape.
Whether magician or goblin or elf
He changes his shape till he scarce knows himself.
First he's a twisted thing, coiled as a rope.
Then he's a griffin that glides down the slope
Of the wind, with a flap of his wings and a slap
Of his tail;
Then he's a galleon gone off at full sail
Within hail
Of the moon.
Oh but soon. . . .

Back to his chimney-top, so I suppose,
When the world's waking up, Huffen Puff goes
Ready to pull himself up by his thumbs
As soon as the dusk of another day comes.

159

THE FAIRY PHONE
Clara Edmonds-Hemingway

Out in the garden, from far overhead,
Dangles a spider. She's spinning a thread:
From the far grapevine to rosebush it hung,
Where, through the midsummer breezes it swung.
See, how this linesman now fastens it there?
Even the drowsiest fairy would dare
Lie on a roseleaf, when she is alone,
Languidly yawning, and answer her phone.

PLAYING AT THE WATERFALL
Janet Norris Bangs

"Waterfall, waterfall, murmuring waterfall,
Why must you hurry so into the pool?"
  "Water for fairy folk,
  Fresh for those merry folk,
  Lighter than airy folk,
    Water that's cool."

"Fairy folk, fairy folk, tiny wee, wary folk,
Where are you hiding and where is your home?"
  "Sometimes we're hiding
  Beneath pebbles gliding
  And sometimes we're riding
    A fleck o' the foam."

"Waterfall, waterfall, plash dashing waterfall
Let me go with you, I'm tired of school!"
  "Ask for an oar from the wing of a plover,
  And wrap yourself dry in a four-leaf of clover,
  And hop on a maple leaf, I'll take you over
    And down to the fairies that live in the pool."

160

THE LADY SLIPPER

Rowena Bennett

A fairy found a slipper
A-growing on a stem.
She said, "I think I'll wear it
If I find a pair of them—
A pair of golden slippers
That haven't any zippers,
That haven't bows or laces
To make them tight in places."

A fairy found a slipper
A-waving in the air
But though she looked all over,
Through grasses and through clover,
She couldn't find a *pair*.
She said: "I must be stopping
This hunting and this shopping,
I really can't go hopping
On one foot everywhere."

And so she ran off barefoot
And when she felt the dews
Between her toes, she said, "I s'pose
It's best to *not* wear shoes."

ROSES

Mary F. Butts

"It is summer," said the fairy,
"Bring me tissue light and airy;
Bring me colors of the rarest,
Search the rainbow for the fairest
Seashell pink and sunny yellow,
Kingly crimson, deep and mellow . . .
Bring me diamonds, shining brightly
Where the morning dew lies lightly . . .
With an art no fay discloses
I am going to make some roses!"

161

THE WITCH OF WILLOWBY WOOD
Rowena Bennett

There once was a witch of Willowby Wood,
and a weird wild witch was she, with hair that was snarled
and hands that were gnarled, and a kickety, rickety
knee. She could jump, they say,
to the moon and back, but this I never did see.
Now Willowby Wood was near Sassafras Swamp,
where there's never a road or rut. And there by the
singing witch-hazel bush the old woman builded
her hut. She builded with neither a hammer or shovel. She
kneaded, she rolled out, she baked
her brown hovel. For *all* witches' houses, I've oft heard
it said, are made of stick candy and fresh
gingerbread. But the shingles that shingled this old
witch's roof were lollipop shingles and hurricane-proof, too
hard to be pelted and melted by rain.
(Why this is important, I soon will explain.)
One day there came running to Sassafras Swamp a dark little
shadowy mouse. He was noted for being a scoundrel
and scamp. And he gnawed at the old woman's house where the
doorpost was weak and the doorpost was worn.
And when the witch scolded, he laughed her to scorn.
And when the witch chased him, he felt quite delighted. She
never could catch him for she was nearsighted. And so,
though she quibbled, he gnawed and he nibbled.
The witch said, "I won't have my house
take a tumble. I'll search in my magical book for a spell
I can weave and a charm I can mumble to get you
away from this nook. It will be a good warning to other
bad mice, who won't earn their bread
but go stealing a slice."
"Your charms cannot hurt," said the mouse, looking pert.
Well, she looked in her book and she
waved her right arm, and she said the most magical
things. Till the mouse, feeling strange,
looked about in alarm, and found he was growing some

wings. He flapped and he fluttered the longer she muttered.
"And now, my fine fellow,
you'd best be aloof," said the witch as he floundered
around. "You can't stay on earth and you
can't gnaw my roof. It's lollipop-hard and it's
hurricane-proof. So you'd better take off
from the ground. If you are wise, stay in the skies."
Then in went the woman of Willowby Wood,
in to her hearthstone and cat.
There she put her old volume up high on the shelf, and
fanned her hot face with her hat. Then she said,
"That is *that*! I have just made a *bat*!"

TREE HOUSE

Mildred Bowers Armstrong

High up a ladder in a cherry tree
Was a little house built just for me.
But when the tree was white with bloom
The redbirds flew into my room.
And when the tree was red with cherries
I entertained the birds and fairies.

Fairies are scarcer now, I know,
And the cherry tree is white with snow—
But even today a bird or an elf
Could make my house a home for himself.

THE FIDGITY FAIRY

Ruth Dixon

There once was a very
Young fidgity fairy,
Who tickled the chin
Of a fussy old fish,
Who then gave a giggle,
A gulp and a wriggle
And left her with only—
His swish!

163

NATURALLY ENOUGH

Berton Braley

Oh, once I knew a merry man
  I met upon my trails,
An Irishman, a Kerry man,
A most extraordinary man
  Who told me fairy tales!

He told me of a river
  That was full of Hudson seals
Which he used to feed on liver
  And on jellyfish and eels,
Till the river was a-quiver
  As they gobbled up their meals.
He was a blithe and airy man
  And when my life a bore is
I think about that merry man
  Who told me fairy stories!

He told me once, this merry man,
  (Unless my memory fails)
He knew an ancient dairyman,
A milkman—mercenary man—
  Who sold the milk of whales.

164

"He used to milk 'em daily,"
  Said this merry man to me,
"While their calves were sportin' gaily,
  Which would do you good to see;
And each faithful father whale, he
  Waited patient as could be!"
That's what he said, that Kerry man,
  And when my temper sore is,
I think about that merry man
  Who told me fairy stories.

He was a card, that merry man,
  My laughter comes in gales
When I recall that Kerry man,
That most extraordinary man
  Who told me fairy tales!

And were they pure inventions,
  All these stories he'd aver?
I don't know his intentions
  But I rather think they were,
For the scripture often mentions
  That a mortal's prone to err.
And though he was a merry man,
A canny and a wary man,
  He also was a ferryman
  Who, when he gets ashore, is
Undoubtedly the *very* man
  To tell you fairy stories!

FAIRIES*

Hilda Conkling

I cannot see fairies.
I dream them.
There is no fairy can hide from me;
I keep on dreaming till I find him:
There you are, Primrose! I see you, Black Wing!

THE SPELL

Ruth Dixon

The boy who lives at Jones's
    And has the reddish hair
Says, "Shucks, the fairies don't
    Live anywhere!"
And he *won't* believe in brownies,
    Just laughs. Do you suppose
That *they* wished all those freckles
    On his nose?

FAIRY LORE

Rose Fyleman

Fairies learn to dance before they learn to walk;
Fairies learn to sing before they learn to talk;
Fairies learn their counting from the cuckoo's call;
    They do not learn Geography at all.

Fairies go a-riding with witches on their brooms
And steal away the rainbows to brighten up their rooms;
Fairies like a sky-dance better than a feast;
    They have a birthday once a week at least.

Fairies think the rain as pretty as the sun;
Fairies think that trespass-boards are only made for fun;
Fairies think that peppermint's the nicest thing they know;
    I *always* take a packet when I go.

*Reprinted by permission of the publishers, J. B. Lippincott Company, from *Poems by a Little Girl*, by Hilda Conkling. Copyright, 1920, by J. B. Lippincott Company.

ELIZABETH ORTON JONES

SEA CHILD

Nancy Byrd Turner

Mermie was a sea child,
The cheerfulest of girls;
For a game of marbles
She had to use pearls.
She slept upon a coral bed,
Her toys were rather few,
But when she couldn't have a doll
She'd make a dolphin do.

THE MERMAIDENS

Laura E. Richards

The little white mermaidens live in the sea,
In a palace of silver and gold;
And their neat little tails are all covered with scales,
Most beautiful for to behold.

On wild white horses they ride, they ride,
And in chairs of pink coral they sit;
They swim all the night, with a smile of delight,
And never feel tired a bit.

THE LITTLE GNOME

Laura E. Richards

Once there lived a little gnome
Who had made his little home
Right down in the middle of the earth, earth, earth.
He was full of fun and frolic,
But his wife was melancholic,
And he never could divert her into mirth, mirth, mirth.

He had tried her with a monkey
And a parrot and a donkey,
And a pig that squealed whene'er he pulled its tail, tail, tail.
But though he laughed himself
Into fits, the jolly elf,
Still his wifey's melancholy did not fail, fail, fail.

"I will hie me," said the gnome,
"From my worthy earthy home;
I will go among the dwellings of the men, men, men.
Something funny there must be,
That will make her say 'He, he!'
I will find it and will bring it her again, 'gain, 'gain."

So he traveled here and there,
And he saw the Blinking Bear,
And the Pattypol whose eyes are in his tail, tail, tail.
And he saw the Linking Gloon,
Who was playing the bassoon,
And the Octopus a-waltzing with the whale, whale, whale.

168

He saw the Chingo Chee,
And a lovely sight was he,
With a ringlet and a ribbon on his nose, nose, nose,
And the Baggle, and the Wogg,
And the Cantilunar Dog,
Who was throwing cotton-flannel at his foes, foes, foes.

All these the little gnome
Transported to his home,
And set them down before his weeping wife, wife, wife;
But she only cried and cried,
And she sobbywobbed and sighed,
Till she really was in danger of her life, life, life.

Then the gnome was in despair,
And he tore his purple hair,
And he sat him down in sorrow on a stone, stone, stone.
"I, too," he said, "will cry,
Till I tumble down and die,
For I've had enough of laughing all alone, 'lone, 'lone."

His tears they flowed away,
Like a rivulet at play,
With a bubble, gubble, rubble, o'er the ground, ground, ground.
But when this his wifey saw,
She loudly cried, "Haw, haw!
Here at last is something funny you have found, found, found."

She laughed, "Ho, ho! he, he!"
And she chuckled loud with glee,
And she wiped away her little husband's tears, tears, tears.
And since then, through wind and weather,
They have said "He, he!" together,
For several hundred thousand merry years, years, years.

mister mckee

169

SNOWFLAKE FUN

Ruth Dixon

Flutterfly and Silver Wing
Tinkle Toes and Twink
Came frolicking and rollicking
As quick as any wink,
And off their shining silver sleigh
They fluttered in the air,
As frosty fairies always do,
And somersaulted there!

In a glimmering and shimmering
Of twirly whirly snow,
They tossed some little frosty flakes
On children down below;
And these were fairy valentines,
I really truly think,
From Flutterfly and Silver Wing
And Tinkle Toes and Twink!

THE LIGHT–HEARTED FAIRY

Author Unknown

Oh, who is so merry, so merry, heigh ho!
As the light-hearted fairy? heigh ho!
       Heigh ho!
   He dances and sings
   To the sound of his wings,
With a hey and a heigh and a ho!
Oh, who is so merry, so airy, heigh ho!
As the light-hearted fairy? heigh ho!
       Heigh ho!
   His nectar he sips
   From the primrose's lips
With a hey and a heigh and a ho!
Oh, who is so merry, so merry, heigh ho!
As the light-footed fairy? heigh ho!
       Heigh ho!
   The night is his noon
   And the sun is his moon,
With a hey and a heigh and a ho!

170

THE WIND ELVES
Ruth Dixon

Three little elves
Sailed away by themselves,
Hippity—hoppity—ho!
They bought a balloon
From the Man in the Moon
Once in a dream long ago,
And out in the wind
They wiggled and spinned
Around and around in a row.

Three little elves
Had fun by themselves,
Hippity—hoppity—hi!
Their furs kept them warm,
As they skid through a storm
Up in the cold gray sky.
And each had a bunch
Of moonbeams for lunch
And a nibble of Pixieland pie.

Three little elves
Then sang to themselves,
Hippity—hoppity—hee!
And after a ride
On a rainbow slide
They fell through the air—*whee-ee*
And landed *ker-flop*
On the tippity-top
Of their favorite Rockabye Tree!

171

CANDLEBRIGHT, CANDLELIGHT!

Ivy O. Eastwick

Candlebright,
Candlelight,
What way swings
The moon tonight?

From the East
To West, my dears,
From the East to West,
So that there is moonlight in
Every brown bird's nest.

Candlelight,
Candlebright,
What way swings
The moon tonight?

From the West
To East, my dear,
From the West to East,
So there's silver light upon
The fairies' woodland feast.

THE APPLE RHYME

Madeleine Nightingale

In my garden grows a tree
Of apple-blossom, where for me
A blackbird perches every day,
Sings his song and flies away.
So since fairies make for birds
Music out of fairy words,
I have learned from it a rhyme
For folk to sing at appletime,
Which, (if you live where apples
    grow),
You'll find a useful thing to know:

Apples ripe and apples red,
Grow they high above my head.
Alack-a-day! for I am small
And apple trees are mostly tall;
Dreary-me! But what is sadder,
Nobody can find a ladder.
Call a pixy, green or brown,
And bid him throw the apples down.
Pixy, throw them down as quick
Or quicker than my hands could pick!
One, two, three, and now another,
Each one bigger than the other.
Pixies green and pixies brown,
Throw the big red apples down.

POOKA

Ella Young

Joyous-footed,
White as snow,
Where the winds go
You go,
Pooka,
Dancing.

In a curving wave
Curved like a cave
In a green sea-hollow
You hide and play:
You slip away
Too swift for us to follow.

But at times it chances we,
Beneath a tree,
Or where foam-bubbles slide
On edges of the tide,
See tracks of where you ran:
Little goat-hoof prints of Pan,
Your footprints,
Pooka.

THE ORGAN GRINDERS' GARDEN
Mildred Plew Meigs

In the winter, in the winter,
   When the clouds shake snow,
I know a little garden
   Where the organ grinders go;

A cozy little garden
   Where the fountain makes a fizz,
And round about the lattices
   The sunbeams sizz;

Where underneath the bushes
   In the nodding afternoons,
The frisky little organs sit
   And spill their tinky tunes;

While tingle, tingle, tangle,
   Go the pennies in the cup,
As all the baby monkeys
   Practice picking pennies up.

In the winter, in the winter,
   When the sharp winds blow,
I know a little garden
   Where the organ grinders go;

A giddy little garden
   Where the fruit is always ripe,
And every grinning grinder
   Sits and pulls upon a pipe;

While all the father monkeys
  Hang their fezzes on the twigs,
And teach the baby monkeys
  How to master little jigs;

Until at last the mothers come,
  As day begins to fade,
And tuck the baby monkeys up
  To snoozle in the shade.

In the winter, in the winter,
  When the clouds shake snow,
I know a little garden
  Where the organ grinders go;

A garden where the grinders
  And the monkeys on a string,
Are pleased to wait serenely
  For the coming of the spring.

THE CHILD AND THE FAIRIES
Author Unknown

The woods are full of fairies!
  The trees are all alive;
The river overflows with them,
  See how they dip and dive!
What funny little fellows!
  What dainty little dears!
They dance and leap, and prance
      and peep,
  And utter fairy cheers!

I'd like to tame a fairy,
  To keep it on a shelf,
To see it wash its little face,
  And dress its little self.
I'd teach it pretty manners,
  It always should say, "Please!"
And then, you know, I'd make it sew,
  And curtsy with its knees!

175

Part V: UNDER THE SKY

WISE

Aileen Fisher

Whoever planned
the world was wise
to think of land,
and seas, and skies,

To plan a sun
and moon that could
be made to run
the way they should.

But how did He
have time for all
the things we see
that are so small—

Like flowers in parks,
and flakes of snow,
and little sparks
the fireflies show?

176

MORNING*
Hilda Conkling

There is a brook I must hear
Before I go to sleep.
There is a birch tree I must visit
Every night of clearness.
I have to do some dreaming,
I have to listen a great deal,
Before light comes back
By a silver arrow of cloud,
And I rub my eyes and say
It must be morning on this hill!

WHY THE WINDS BLOW
Caroline S. P. Wild

I know!
I know
Why the winds blow:
If the winds didn't blow,
The leaves wouldn't flutter;
If the leaves didn't flutter,
The shadows wouldn't dance!
I love the dancing shadow-leaves,
And that is why I know
It is for my fun with shadows
That the sweet winds blow.

WIND
Mildred Bowers Armstrong

I wish that I could see the wind,
Could look upon her face.
She walks across the tops of trees
With an unfailing grace.
So kindly is Her Majesty,
The smallest flowers and grasses
Bob up and down to welcome her
Everywhere she passes.

*Reprinted by permission of the publishers, J. B. Lippincott Company, from *Poems by a Little Girl*, by Hilda Conkling. Copyright, 1920, by J. B. Lippincott Company.

177

APRIL RAIN

Robert Loveman

It is not raining rain to me,
   It's raining daffodils;
In every dimpled drop I see
   Wild flowers on the hills.

The clouds of gray engulf the day
   And overwhelm the town;
It is not raining rain to me,
   It's raining roses down.

It is not raining rain to me,
   But fields of clover bloom,
Where any buccaneering bee
   Can find a bed and room.

A health unto the happy,
   A fig for him who frets!
It is not raining rain to me,
   It's raining violets.

TAMED

Nancy Byrd Turner

One day in March the boisterous Wind
   Was playing with the weather.
He tossed a fluffy cloud around
   As though it were a feather;
He danced a jig in every tree,
And set the chimneys grumbling
And banged the birds about the sky,
And sent the birdies tumbling.
When April came he roared her name
And loud to meet her rushed
But gentle April smiled and laid
A finger on the lip, and said:
"Now hush, sir!"
          And he hushed.

APRIL
Eunice Tietjens

The tulips now are pushing up
Like small green knuckles through the ground,
The grass is young and doubtful yet.
The robin takes a look around.
And if you listen you can hear
Spring laughing with a windy sound.

TO A VERY YOUNG CLOUD
Ruth Crary

Hurry! Hurry! Little Cloud,
Lagging, lagging far behind
While your brothers push and crowd.
Though you stray, you'll never find
Skyways bluer or more kind.
Do another and another
Somersault, and catch your mother!

THE SUN IS FIRST TO RISE
Elizabeth Coatsworth

Up in the morning early
the sun is first to rise,
the little birds begin to sing,
the farmers rub their eyes.
The rabbits hop down roads of dew,
the new-born baby cries,
and the gray kitten runs and leaps,
chasing white butterflies.

Away to bed with darkness
the sun is first to go,
across the fields with heavy wings
there flaps a shiny crow,
the children put away their toys,
their steps are dragging slow,
and in the woods the spotted fawn
lies close beside the doe.

179

MORNING
Ruth Dixon

The cherry tree's shedding
Its blossoms of May;
Does a Fairyland wedding
Take place today?

Bird babies are coming
And learning to sing,
And the garden's all humming
With spring!

THE PUDDLE
Eleanor Jewett

I found a puddle yesterday
Not bigger than a minute;
And yet it was not very small
For all the sky was in it.

The puddle trembled in the wind,
Afraid that it might dry.
You see, it was so proud to be
The mirror of the sky!

IN GRANDMOTHER'S GARDEN
Faith Baldwin

My grandma's garden, in the Spring,
Is colored like a fairy ring;
Along the paths fat tulips grow,
Like pink balloons set in a row;
And daffodils make sunshine where
Tall lilacs dry their purple hair.

Oh, I can never tell you how
My grandma's flowers nod and bow;
And violets hide in the shade,
As shy as mice and as afraid,
And Easter flower-bonnets gay
Have brand-new trimmings every day!

WHERE DOES MUSIC COME FROM?

Vivian G. Gouled

Where does music come from?
It comes from tapping rain.
It comes from chirping chickadees,
And from the chugging train.

It comes from breaking ocean waves,
It comes from kittens' purrs,
It comes from someone's pleasant voice
And from the wind that stirs.

It comes from chatting katydids,
(A summer evening sound) . . .
Where does the music come from?
It comes from all around!

AFTERNOON

Polly Chase

Barbara sleeps in the pansy bed
And the sunshine tiptoes over her head.
Three petals fall from a yellow rose
And a butterfly lights on the end of her nose.

I NEVER SAW A MOOR
Emily Dickinson

I never saw a moor,
I never saw the sea;
Yet know I how the heather looks,
And what a wave must be.

I never spoke with God,
Nor visited in heaven;
Yet certain am I of the spot
As if the chart were given.

SONG FOR SUMMER
Elizabeth-Ellen Long

I like to water gardens,
I like to watch the hose
In my two hands give beauty
To every waiting rose.

I like to water gardens,
I like to see each tree
Cool in leaf and root because
Of something done by me.

NOCTURNE
Elizabeth-Ellen Long

From where the Night has placed it
On the West's dark window sill,
The silver lamp of Venus
Shines down on field and hill,

Brightening the evening going
And coming of each mouse
And showing the late rabbit
The way to his own house.

182

IN THE GARDEN
Elizabeth Coatsworth

Violets, daffodils,
Roses and thorn
Were all in the garden
Before you were born.
Daffodils, violets,
Green thorn and roses
Your grandchildren's children
Will hold to their noses.

COOL
[A Mid-Summer Song]
Elizabeth-Ellen Long

These words in themselves are cool;
Moss and fern and brook and pool,
Moonlight, starlight, silver, shade,
Meadow, shadow, glen and glade,
Lake and forest, garden, lawn,
Morning, evening, dusk and dawn,
Crystal, frosty, limpid, lave,
Cloister, tunnel, cellar, cave,
Opal, jade, pearl and coral,
Maple, elm, lilac, laurel,

Lattice, trellis, arbor, bower,
Fog and cloud and wind and shower,
Melon, mango, lemon, lime,
Water cress and mint and thyme,
Foam and flotsam, wave and sea,
Columbine, anemone,
Lace and gauze, gossamer, tulle,
These words in themselves are cool!

183

SONG OF GRAY THINGS

Elizabeth-Ellen Long

In any weather, any day,
Much is lovely that is gray;
Driftwood smoothed to satin by
The tide's cool fingers, early sky,
Lichen stars that lightly dapple
Stone-walls around an apple
Orchard, birch-bark and the thin
Warped rails of fences holding in
Reluctant meadows, kittens' fur,
Dried wild grasses sweet as myrrh,
As well as cobweb lace on eaves,
Sudden wind in willow leaves,
And pigeons proudly marching down
The slanted roofs of any town.

WHITE

Elizabeth-Ellen Long

Let's sing a song of white things,
Of breaking waves and gull-wings,
Blowing sheets on Monday's lines,
Lace around red valentines,
Plum-tree blossom, cherry, pear,
Forehead stars black ponies wear,
Christening robes, old ladies' curls,
And petticoats of little girls.

Let's sing a song of white things,
Of milkweed down and smoke rings,
Soapsuds, clover, clouds and sails,
Wedding cakes and bridal veils,
Sifted flour, falling snow,
Berries on green mistletoe,
Summer daisy, winter moon,
And lilies in a blue lagoon.

184

THE NIGHT WILL NEVER STAY*

Eleanor Farjeon

The night will never stay,
The night will still go by,
Though with a million stars
You pin it to the sky,
Though you bind it with the blowing wind
And buckle it with the moon,
The night will slip away
Like sorrow or a tune.

SUMMER

Elizabeth-Ellen Long

I met her down a country road,
A gypsy with a pack
Of lovely things for country-folk,
And cried, "The Summer's back!"

The Summer peddling Queen Anne's lace
And fine embroideries
Of daisies and of clover bloom
And butterflies and bees.

I met her down a country road
Tempting passerby
With wind-frilled leaves and fringed green grass
And lengths of blue silk sky,

Tempting passersby to spend
A moment on such pretties
As never yet were bought or sold
In the shops of cities.

*Reprinted by permission of the publishers, J. B. Lippincott Company, from *Eleanor Farjeon's Poems for Children.* Copyright, 1951, by Eleanor Farjeon.

185

SOMETHING TOLD
THE WILD GEESE

Rachel Field

Something told the wild geese
   It was time to go.
Though the fields lay golden
   Something whispered,—"Snow."
Leaves were green and stirring,
   Berries, luster-glossed,
But beneath warm feathers
   Something cautioned,—"Frost."
All the sagging orchards
   Steamed with amber spice,
But each wild breast stiffened
   At remembered ice.
Something told the wild geese
   It was time to fly,—
Summer sun was on their wings,
   Winter in their cry.

AT NIGHT

Elizabeth-Ellen Long

While we lie sleeping who can say
What silent strangers pass our way,
Slow moths on velvet wings and snails,
Blazing the dark with silver trails,

Crickets who try the quiet for size,
And hop toads wearing jeweled eyes.
While we lie sleeping who can know
What unseen travelers come and go.

IF ONCE YOU HAVE SLEPT ON AN ISLAND
Rachel Field

If once you have slept on an island
    You'll never be quite the same;
You may look as you looked the day before
    And go by the same old name.

You may bustle about in street and shop;
    You may sit at home and sew,
But you'll see blue water and wheeling gulls
    Wherever your feet may go.

You may chat with the neighbors of this and that
    And close to your fire keep,
But you'll hear ship whistle and lighthouse bell
    And tides beat through your sleep.

Oh, you won't know why, and you can't say how
    Such change upon you came,
But—once you have slept on an island
    You'll never be quite the same!

RAINY DAY
Agnes Louise Dean

Down in the passage closet, upon the topmost shelf,
Are special toys for rainy days I cannot reach myself.

They won't come down for cloudy skies, nor yet for
    scatter drops,
There has to be an all day pour—the kind that never stops.

The eavespouts cough and gurgle, the flooded gutters roar,
The rain pelts down the windowpanes, while I lie on the floor

And paint in jolly painting books, and mess with pots and paste.
I cut out scrapbook boys and girls from advertising waste

That Mother saves in careful piles for such a day as this.
If it were sunny all the time, what loads of fun I'd miss!

There are some special dishes for a rainy evening's tea—
A china set that Mother had when she was young like me—

And every rainy suppertime three candles small I light
To take the place of sunset skies upon a rainy night.

AUTUMN

Emily Dickinson

The morns are meeker than they were,
The nuts are getting brown;
The berry's cheek is plumper,
The rose is out of town.

The maple wears a gayer scarf,
The field a scarlet gown.
Lest I should be old-fashioned,
I'll put a trinket on.

PATHS

Josephine Van Dolzen Pease

After the storm,
I love the sand,
So smooth to walk,
An untrod land;
And the leaping, laughing
Edge of the sea,
A wonderful way
To go, for me!
But rather I'd hear,
Along the street,
October's rustle
Beneath my feet!

189

RAIN

Ella Young

Dancing, dancing down the street,
Comes the rain on silver feet:
O hush, O hush,
For the wind is fluting a song.

Little flute of the wind,
Little flute of the wind,
Little flute of the wind,
Play on.

Silver feet of the rain
Come again, come again,
Come with a fluting song.

THE RAIN TOYS

Mildred Bowers Armstrong

Whenever it rains I dress up quaintly in Grandmother's slippers and a great-aunt's gown;
I write long letters with my fat, red pencil, or I read
from a book held upside down.

Whenever it storms I stand by the window, watching the
raindrops hold a race.
I mix soap bubbles in a pan of water. I look in the
mirror while I crinkle my face.

When it rains much longer than it ever should rain, and
I can't help whining and I just must pout,
Mother reaches up in the deep, black cupboard and pulls
a few of the rain toys out—

Bright-colored paper—a dog on a string—blocks—a
clown—a wagon and a train—
New toys and old toys I haven't seen for weeks, and then
I don't care if we do have rain!

190

SPLINTER

Carl Sandburg

The voice of the last cricket
across the first frost
is one kind of good-bye.
It is so thin a splinter of singing.

CORN IN THE SHOCKS

Katharine Ellis Barrett

Corn-shock tepees,
    Dry rattling sound,
Trees all scalped,
    Leaves on the ground,
Stealthy approach of winter's cold,
The year grown gaunt and sere and old—
    Indians must be around.

SILVER TREES

Aileen Fisher

In the fall I saw some trees
with silver leaves, with silver leaves.
From a distance they were quite
as silver as a lake at night.
But closer up I saw that they
were silver-green and silver-white.
In the fall I saw some leaves
on silver trees, on silver trees.
And then I thought, "When they are gone
and snow and ice fall down upon
the branches and the twigs some day,
the trees will STILL have silver on."

191

FIELD FLOWERS

Eleanor Jewett

They grow by the side of the road,
  Goldenrod, clover, and grass.
Free they are as the gypsy trail
  That winds through a mountain pass.

Free as the birds and the star-dewed nights
  That God in his grace has given
To him with the heart for the seeing of things
  Where things go their way undriven.

By the side of the road they grow,
  Goldenrod, grass—and clover—
Where the trail winds away to the end of the world
  And the sumac arches over.

IN FROM THE SEA

Elizabeth Coatsworth

This air that blows in from the sea
No one has breathed before
Save only porpoises as they play
In waves far out from shore,
Or whales whose tranquil breathings rise
In fountains of white spray,
Or sailors leaning on the rails
Of ships from far away.
Sea gulls with nostrils of strong bone
Have tasted this keen breeze,
And gannets in their billowing flight,
But nothing less than these—
Nothing save creatures strong and wild
As vigorous and free,
Themselves, as is the wind that blows
So coldly from the sea.

FOG

Carl Sandburg

The fog comes
on little cat feet.

It sits looking
over harbor and city
on silent haunches
and then moves on.

THE GREAT CRAFTSMAN

Mildred Bowers Armstrong

Who set the wings on butterflies
And gave the spiders lace to make,
At evening put the wren to sleep
And kept the katydid awake?

He also sealed the pool one night
And gave the squirrel a thicker coat.
He tucked the rose roots under leaves
And gave wild duck a calling note.

He sent a bit of snow then,
The largest, whitest flakes He had,
To decorate the cornstalks
And make the children glad.

BEDTIME FOR A BABY BROOK

Ruth Crary

The weary little brook, when snows begin,
Draws up his icy sheet beneath his chin;
Then snuggles down, tucks fleecy blankets in,
Settling himself to sleep till spring—the sigh
Of crystal-laden winds, his lullaby;
His nurse, the white-starched moon in a brooding sky.

193

THE MIST AND ALL

Dixie Willson

I like the fall,
The mist and all.
I like the night owl's
Lonely call—
And wailing sound
Of wind around.
I like the gray
November day,
And bare, dead boughs
That coldly sway
Against my pane.
I like the rain.
I like to sit
And laugh at it—
And tend
My cozy fire a bit.
I like the fall—
The mist and all—

AUTUMN SONG

Elizabeth-Ellen Long

These are the days of fallen leaves,
The days of hazy weather,
Smelling of gold chrysanthemums
And gray wood-smoke together.

These are the nights of nearby stars,
The nights of closer moons,
When the windy darkness echoes
To crickets' farewell tunes.

194

REMEMBERING THE WINTER

Rowena Bennett

Remembering the winter, the squirrel goes nutting
Up where the branches of the hickory are jutting,
Over where the butternut boughs are tossing . . .
(The air is a canyon that the squirrel is crossing.)
Down the oak-tree's ladder he hurries to deposit
All his buried treasure in the earth's safe closet . . .
Remembering the winter.

Remembering the winter, the birds go winging,
(No time for nesting, no time for singing.)
Sailing to the southward with wings for sails,
Steering through emptiness with long, rudder tails.
Traveling, traveling, days and days,
With no map to guide them through the wide, wild ways.

Remembering the winter, the bear finds a hollow
In a dry cavern where none dares to follow.
Where even the icicle cannot push its splinter. . . .
Oh, wise are the wild things, preparing for the winter!

SNOWY MORNING

Frances Frost

Wake up! Hurry! Jump from bed!
Race for the window! Press your nose
against the pane! No sun! Instead
it's snowing! All the white sky blows
glitter across the drifting hill!
Get dressed! Hurry! Run for the shed!
The snow heaps high on the window sill!
Where's the toboggan? Where's the sled?
Plunge into whiteness, race through sky
that dances, whirls in the dizzy air!
Coast down the lovely morning, fly
with silver stars in your eyes and hair!

SING HO!

Jeanne De Lamarter

Sing ho for the snow
    white stars and feathers!
Winter is one of my
    favorite weathers!

THE BUNNY

Adelaide Love

I saw a small brown bunny run
Across the winter snow
And wondered where he lived and why
He had to hurry so.

Perhaps he had stayed out too long
And Mother Bunny'd scold;
Perhaps he hurried home because
His little feet were cold.

KING QUIET

Carolyn Forsyth

Quietly the winter
    Comes in shoes of satin
With no bird to sing him
    A vesper or a matin,
With gardens, though, to greet him,
    Delicate and white,
Of little frost flowers
    That bloom overnight—
Little frost flowers
    On all the window grasses
To greet the silent winter
    With silence as he passes.

INQUISITIVE BARN

Frances Frost

The white-housed village
In a featherbed
Sleeps with snow
About its head.

The only thing
In all this white
That keeps its lifting
Glow in sight

Is our old barn
That, loving fun,
Pokes its red head
Into the sun.

NEW SNOW

Frances Frost

All in the feathery weather,
into the light new snow,
into the cloud-stars flying,
gaily the small cats go.

For the first time, prancing sideways,
their tails puffed with surprise,
the little cats gaze skyward
with blue astonished eyes.

Each infant black imp scampers
like a delirious leaf;
but when he sits in silver,
his sitting-down is brief!

All in the feathery weather,
snow-booted black paws come
bringing three sets of whiskers
on star-wet faces home.

197

WINTER WOOD

Eleanor Elizabeth Stevens

Wind and bird and brook are still,
Frosty hush on every hill!
Quiet as I can I go
Up this quiet steep of snow,
Lest I break, with step or sigh,
What other creatures, less than I,
Keep in awed and gentled mood:
Silence of a winter wood.

WHITE FIELDS

James Stephens

In the wintertime we go
Walking in the fields of snow;

Where there is no grass at all;
Where the top of every wall,

Every fence, and every tree,
Is as white as white can be.

Pointing out the way we came,
—Everyone of them the same—

All across the fields there be
Prints in silver filigree;

And our mothers always know,
By the footprints in the snow,

Where it is the children go.

198

FIRST SNOWFALL
Elizabeth-Ellen Long

Now Snow, the white magician,
With no one's help at all,
Makes a sagging barn into
An alabaster hall,

Then puts a crystal tower
Where late a silo stood,
And turns to silver ingots
Stacked piles of kindling wood.

Now Snow, the white magician,
Without your aid or mine,
Makes of every muddy pool
A lace-frilled Valentine,

Strings jeweled garlands lightly
Between tall wayside poles
And dresses shabby haystacks
In royal ermine stoles!

IT'S SNOWING!
Adelaide Love

It's snowing! It's snowing! And I'm going out
Where the snow is the deepest to tumble about.

I'll roll a great snowball as big as myself
That will look like a world to a wee winter elf.

I'll make a great snow man (Oh, very much taller
Than I) and his wife who will be a bit smaller.

What fun I shall have until Mother calls: "Better
Come in now before your clothes get any wetter."

But, before I go in to dry off my things,
I'll lie in the snow and make angels with wings!

199

Part VI: JUST FUN

JONATHAN BING DANCES FOR SPRING
Beatrice Curtis Brown

Blow the fife and clarinet,
Let the band advance!
Mr. Bing will welcome Spring
With his festive dance!

Waking with the sunshine,
Starting out of sleep;
Flings away the blanket gray,
Makes a mighty leap—

Leaps upon the mantelpiece,
Bounces up again,
Turns about and dashes out
Through the windowpane:

All the neighbors' children
Clap and shout, "Hooray!"
When Mr. B., in highest glee
Comes prancing down the way.

Who can ever stop him?
Who so fast as Bing?
When hop and prance, he does his dance
To celebrate the Spring.

Hop! He's on a treetop.
Bump! He's on the tiles.
Bounce and vault and somersault,
He goes for miles and miles.

200

The motorcars are hooting;
The whistles all a-blow,
They holler, "Hi!" as Bing goes by,
"Say, where d'you think you go?"

The Lord Mayors of the city
In velvet cloak and chain
Appear in state, expostulate
With Bing—but all in vain.

"Away, you foolish creatures!"
Cries happy Mr. Bing.
"With all this fun of flowers and sun,
Who would not dance for Spring?"

THE PURPLE–EYED PIRATE

Marjorie Barrows

There once was a purple-eyed pirate
　On the top of a tropical hill,
Who played on his tremulous trombone
　To his pedigreed parakeet, Bill.

And he played till he blew up a cyclone
　That left but a dirk and a quill
Of the picturesque purple-eyed pirate
　And his pedigreed parakeet, Bill.

BEDTIME STORY

Rowena Bennett

There once were some llamas
Who didn't have mamas
To make them pajamas
　　To sleep in at night.
They said, "We shan't worry.
Our coats are all furry,
And in a snow flurry
　　When hillsides are white,
It would be quite silly
And just a bit chilly
　　(Though very polite)
To wear pants and blouses
Like people in houses.
We'd much rather wear
(Since we're out in the air)
A blanket of hair
　　And be bundled up tight.
"So," finished the llamas,
"We do not need mamas
To make us pajamas
　　To sleep in at night."

202

GEOGRAPHY LESSON
Rowena Bennett

The Eskimos have frosted toes.
 Their land is never hot.
Their igloo homes have icy domes
 Beneath which they must squat.
They fish and hunt
And mostly grunt
 And like their life a lot.
 (The Hottentot does not.)

The Eskimoses
All rub noses
 (That's their way of kissing).
No one supposes
Eskimoses
 Guess what they are missing.
(The Hottentot, I 'most forgot
Is hot, but really not a tot.)

The Eskimos live where it snows.
 They have no garden plot.
On winter nights the Northern Lights
 Dress up their lonely spot.
The Eskimos wear lots of clothes;
 (The Hottentot does not.)

OCELOT
Clara E. Randall

I don't know if you have or not
Ever seen an ocelot.
Of the pussy family, he
Has grace and much agility.
His fur is very soft and yet
He would not make a suitable pet.

203

THE ANIMALS' FAIR

Carolyn Wells

'Twas long ago, they say, in the Land of Far-Away,
   The beasties clubbed together and they held a big bazaar;
Not an animal was slighted, every single one invited,
   And they all appeared delighted as they came from near and far.

The bear brushed his hair and dressed himself with care,
   With the Lynx and two Minks he started to the fair;
The Tapir cut a caper as he read his morning paper,
   And learned about the great bazaar and all the wonders there.

The chattering Chinchilla trotted in with the Gorilla,
   Much elated, so they stated, by the prospect of the fun;
While the Yak, dressed in black, came riding in a hack,
   And the Buffalo, would scuffle, oh,—because he couldn't run.

The Donkey told the Monkey that he had forgot his trunk key,
   So an Ox took the box, and put it in the way
Of a passing Hippopotamus, who angrily said, "What a muss!"
   As he trod upon the baggage and observed the disarray.

Graceful little Antelope bought a delicious cantaloupe,
    And at table with a Sable sat primly down to eat;
While a frisky young Hyena coyly gave a philopena
    To an Ibex who made shy becks at her from across the street.

A Bison was a-pricin' a tea-chest of young hyson,
    So cheap, said the Sheep, that it nearly made her weep;
The lazy Armadillo bought a satin sofa-pillow,
    Then found a cozy, dozy place and laid him down to sleep.

An inhuman old Ichneumon sang a serenade by Schumann,
    The Giraffe gave a laugh and began to cheer and chaff;
A laughing Jaguar said, "My, what a wag you are!"
    And the Camel got his camera and took a photograph.

The Baboon and the Loon and the rollicking Raccoon
    Fed an Otter with a blotter, though it wasn't good to eat;
The Bunny thought 'twas funny all his money went for honey,
    But a Rabbit has a habit of liking what is sweet.

The Ape left her cape out on the fire-escape,
    The Jerboa lost her boa, which caused her much distress;
But the fair was well attended and the money well expended,
    And financially and socially it was a great success.

HOW TO GET TO ITALY
Aileen Fisher

Old Mr. Smithers, alas,
found his automobile out of gas.
And since he was due up at Baraboo,
he thought he would ride on his caribou.

Old Mr. Smithers, alack,
climbed up on his caribou's back.
But the animal sprinted so prettily,
it landed Old Smithers in Italy.

Old Mr. Smithers, oh dear,—
the moral of this story is clear:
If *you* have a date up in Baraboo,
don't go for a ride on your caribou.

THE ELEPHANT IN THE CINNAMON TREE
Leroy F. Jackson

Away down south by the Southern Sea
An elephant sits in a cinnamon tree.
He's a thousand miles from the nearest town,
He can't get up and he can't get down,
So that's the reason, you must agree,
The elephant sits in the cinnamon tree.

CATASTROPHE!!
Malcolm Douglas

Said a thousand-legged worm,
As he gave a great squirm,
"Has anyone seen a leg of mine?
If it can't be found
I'll have to get round
With only nine hundred and ninety-nine!"

THE MAID OF TIMBUCTOO

Laura E. Richards

A lovely maid of Timbuctoo
She loved a Bedouin so true,
She stole her uncle's choicest scarab
To buy tobacco for her Arab.
Sing ha ha ha and hoo hoo hoo!
The lovely maid of Timbuctoo!

Her uncle was a savage chief;
He swore he'd thwack the rascal thief
Who stole withouten dread or fear
The beetle that he held so dear.
Sing ha ha ha and hoo hoo hoo!
The lovely maid of Timbuctoo!

The maid crept out, her love to see;
The uncle followed after she,
And saw her give, and heard her tell
About the deed she'd planned so well.
Sing ha ha ha and hoo hoo hoo!
The lovely maid of Timbuctoo!

He took a cudgel new and stout,
And wound it all with cords about,
And 'neath a palm tree's shady cover
He thwacked the maiden and her lover.
Sing ha ha ha and hoo hoo hoo!
The lovely maid of Timbuctoo!

MORAL

Maids! If your uncle is an Arab,
Don't steal his highly valued scarab,
Or you may meet in palmy shade
The fate that met this hapless maid.
Sing ha ha ha and hoo hoo hoo!
The lovely maid of Timbuctoo!

BELINDA

Marjorie Barrows

Belinda was a very bashful whale,
Who blubbered when she tried to sing a scale,
And when, against her wishes,
She'd meet a school of fishes,
She always tried to hide behind her tail!

THE SENSIBLE LOBSTER

Helen Wing

I knew a young lobster,
    A sensible chap,
Who wore a white apron
    To cover his lap.

He said that he liked it
    Because it was frilly
And kept off the draft
    When the weather was chilly.

OCTOPUS

Adele Jordan Tarr

Oedipus Octopus, living at Shedd,*
Started his life in a deep-sea bed.
One little Oc. in a million or more—
How could he know what fate had in store?
How could he guess how famous he'd be,
Living in glass for a whole world to see?

Oedipus Octopus, eight-legged fish,
You wished to travel—and you got your wish!
Northward you came from your warm Southern Seas,
Here to be coddled and live at your ease—
Special shore-dinners to tempt you each day,—
Lobster and crab on a sea-weed buffet.

*Shedd Aquarium, Chicago, Illinois.

Oedipus Octopus, what's on your mind?
Are you regretting some friend left behind—
Some Octopussy with classical beak?
Sa-a-y! she forgot you the very next week!
Thank Father Neptune who gave you your chance—
Travel—fame—luxury. Who wants romance?

Here, you're Shedd's Biggest Fish. There, you would be
Just one more octopus, under the sea.

THE SHARK

Laura E. Richards

Oh! blithe and merrily sang the shark,
  As he sat on the housetop high:
A-cleaning his boots, and smoking cheroots,
  With a single glass in his eye.

With a handkerchief gay he polished away,
  And a smile on his face did glow,
As merry and bold the chorus he trolled
  Of "Gobble-em-upsky ho!"

He sang so loud, he astonished the crowd
  Which gathered from far and near.
For they said, "Such a sound, in the country round,
  We never, no, never did hear."

210

He sang of the ships that he'd eaten like chips
   In the palmy days of his youth.
And he added, "If you don't believe it is true,
   Pray examine my wisdom tooth!"

He sang of the whales who'd have given their tails
   For a glance of his raven eye.
And the swordfish, too, who their weapons all drew,
   And swor'd for his sake they'd die.

And he sang about wrecks and hurricane decks
   And the mariner's perils and pains,
Till every man's blood up on end it stood,
   And their hair ran cold in their veins.

But blithe as a lark the merry old shark,
   He sat on the sloping roof.
Though he said, "It is queer that no one draws near
   To examine my wisdom toof!"

And he caroled away, by night and by day,
   Until he made every one ill.
And I'll wager a crown that unless he's come down,
   He is probably caroling still.

UNNATURAL HISTORY
Carolyn Wells

THE FLAMINGO

See the Flamingo! All please note
  His wondrous height and girth;
He has the longest legs and throat
  Of anything on earth.
Such throats are trying, are they not,
  In case one catches cold?
Well, yes; but just think what a lot
  His Christmas stockings hold!

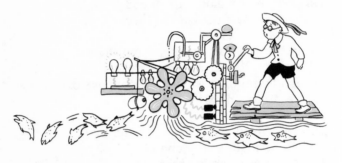

WASTED PHILANTHROPY

His name was Tesla Einstein Edison Marconi Ford;
So naturally, high aloft his young ambitions soared.

He yearned a marvel to invent which would bring fame to him,
So he devised a gadget which would teach the fish to swim.

'Twas very complicated, with levers, pulleys, strings,
Ratchets and cogs and angle-irons and many suchlike things;

Designed to make the fish swim straight, not in a wobbly swish,
Eliding much waste motion and encouraging the fish.

At last the thing was finished, a magnificent affair,
A perfect mechanism—the fish came round to stare;

But after one brief glance, they swam away—with zigzag movement;
Haughtily scorning all the efforts made for their improvement!

212

A BEAST I LIKE

I'm fond of the Iguanodon,
  We have a lot in common;
He's never been to Carcassonne,
  I've never met a Brahmin.

I honor the Iguanodon,
  I'm sure I wish him well;
But I wish he had been born Anon—
  He is so hard to spell!

THE QUEER ONE

There's a queer little fairy or pixy or sprite,
They call him a djinn, and that is all right;
For that is his name, but it does seem to me
They might leave off one N, and scratch out the D.

Well, where do you think that queer little Djinn
Picked out a good place to keep himself in?
Why, he chose a great big empty Djinnger Djar,
On the shelf where the djams and djellies are!

In the djar he djumped and djounced about,
And sometimes stuck his djolly head out;
And one day he djerked himself out of the djar
And said, "I shall go on a djourney afar."

A djolting djinriksha appeared at the door,
My Djinn djust djumped in—so my djingle is o'er.

213

IF I WERE A ONE-LEGGED PIRATE

Mildred Plew Meigs

If I were a one-legged pirate
  Ga-lumping around on a peg,
I'd flourish my pistol and fire it;
  Then, sure as my right wooden leg,
I'd buy me a three-decker galleon
  With cannon to port and to lee,
And wearing the king's medallion,
  I'd head for a tropical sea!
Roaring a rough Ha-ha! Ha-ho!
  Roving the routes of old,
Over the billows we would go
  Sweeping the seas for gold!
    Plying the lane
    Of the Spanish Main
     For Gold!
      Gold!
       Gold!

If I were a one-legged pirate
  Ga-lumping around after loot,
I'd flourish my pistol and fire it;
  Then, sure as my red leather boot,
I'd buy me a three-decker galleon
  With cannon to thunder a mile,
And bucking the sea like a stallion,
  I'd head for a tropical isle!
Roaring a rough Ha-ha! Ha-ho!
  Chanting a chantey bold,
Over the billows we would blow,
  Sweeping the seas for gold!
    Plying the lane
    Of the Spanish Main
     For Gold!
      Gold!
       Gold!

But since I was not born a pirate
  Ga-lumping around on a stick;
And since my toy gun when I fire it
  Gives out but a little toy click;
Pretending my boat is a galleon,
  My pond is a tropical sea,
I'll play I'm an old rapscallion,
  But really I won't hurt a flea.
Roaring my small Ha-ha! Ha-ho!
  Saying I'm someone bold,
Over the duck pond I will go
  Roving the routes of old;
     Plying the pond
     And the stream beyond
     For Gold!
      Gold!
       Gold!

THE MISHAPS OF GENTLE JANE
Carolyn Wells

Gentle Jane went walking, where
She espied a Grizzly Bear;
Flustered by the quadruped,
Gentle Jane just lost her head.

Last week Tuesday, gentle Jane
Met a passing railroad train;
"Ah, good afternoon," she said;
But the train just cut her dead.

Jane fell in an awful faint
In a tub of cobalt paint.
When at last she did come to,
Gentle Jane looked rather blue.

Gentle Jane once chanced to sit
Where some rifle-bullets hit.
Though she had no bumps or sprains,
Gentle Jane felt shooting pains.

Up in Harlem wilds remote,
Gentle Jane observed a goat.
Shortly afterward they met—
Gentle Jane was all upset.

From the Flatiron Building's top,
Gentle Jane once chanced to drop.
When she fell into the town
She appeared to be cast down.

When a cyclone struck the place
Gentle Jane was whirled through space.
"It's all right," said Jane, "I know;
But it was an awful blow!"

Gentle Jane, with no one nigh her,
Touched a live electric wire.
As the crowd around her flocked
Gentle Jane seemed rather shocked.

216

ANIMAL CRACKERS

Aileen Fisher

One day two Peruvian llamas
ran away from their papas and mamas,
but they came back at night
because in their flight
they'd forgotten to pack their pajamas.

There once was a weasel named Herman
who said to his cousin, the ermine,
"Why people think mice
don't taste very nice,
it really is hard to determine."

THE CAMEL

Carolyn Wells

The camel is a creature strange,
Across the East he loves to range.
And o'er the desert swiftly hies,
Kicking the East up in your eyes.
If you desire to take a ride,
He kneels, and you climb up outside;
And when you're nicely fixed, why then,
He tumbles you right off again.

DISCOMFORT

Carolyn Wells

The porcupine was fretful,
He really acted dretful,
    He filled the air with whimperings and whines;
This the reason that he gave,
He had had a permanent wave,
    And it gave him curvature of all his spines!

217

THE CAMEL'S COMPLAINT
Charles E. Carryl

"Canary-birds feed on sugar and seed,
 Parrots have crackers to crunch;
And, as for the poodles, they tell me the noodles
 Have chickens and cream for their lunch.
  But there's never a question
  About MY digestion—
   ANYTHING does for me!

"Cats, you're aware, can repose in a chair,
 Chickens can roost upon rails;
Puppies are able to sleep in a stable,
 And oysters can slumber in pails.
  But no one supposes
  A poor Camel dozes—
   ANY PLACE does for me!

"Lambs are inclosed where it's never exposed,
 Coops are constructed for hens;
Kittens are treated to houses well heated,
 And pigs are protected by pens.
  But a Camel comes handy
  Wherever it's sandy—
   ANYWHERE does for me!

"People would laugh if you rode a giraffe,
 Or mounted the back of an ox;
It's nobody's habit to ride on a rabbit,
 Or try to bestraddle a fox.
  But as for a Camel, he's
  Ridden by families—
   ANY LOAD does for me!

"A snake is as round as a hole in the ground,
 And weasels are wavy and sleek;
And no alligator could ever be straighter
 Than lizards that live in a creek.
  But a Camel's all lumpy
  And bumpy and humpy—
   ANY SHAPE does for me!"

LITTLE SUSAN ZEBRA

Jess Dobson Alt

Little Susan Zebra sat
Trying on a summer hat.
"I'll take this hat," Miss Susan said,
"It surely seems to fit my head."
Then she stood up and turned around,
And suddenly Miss Susan frowned,
For she heard someone plainly say,
"We really *don't* wear stripes today."

THE DUEL

Eugene Field

The gingham dog and the calico cat
Side by side on the table sat;
'Twas half past twelve, and (what do you think!)
Nor one nor t'other had slept a wink!
   The old Dutch clock and the Chinese plate
   Appeared to know as sure as fate
There was going to be a terrible spat.
   (I wasn't there: I simply state
   What was told to me by the Chinese plate!)

The gingham dog went, "Bow-wow-wow!"
And the calico cat replied, "Mee-ow!"
The air was littered, an hour or so,
With bits of gingham and calico,

219

While the old Dutch clock in the chimney-place
Up with its hands before its face,
For it always dreaded a family row!
  (*Now mind: I'm only telling you*
  What the old Dutch clock declares is true!)

The Chinese plate looked very blue,
And wailed, "Oh dear! what shall we do!"
But the gingham dog and the calico cat
Wallowed this way and tumbled that,
  Employing every tooth and claw
  In the awfullest way you ever saw—
And, oh! how the gingham and calico flew!
  (*Don't fancy I exaggerate;*
  I got my news from the Chinese plate.)

Next morning where the two had sat
They found no trace of dog nor cat;
And some folks think unto this day
That burglars stole that pair away!
  But the truth about the cat and pup
  Is this: they ate each other up!
Now what do you really think of that!
  (*The old Dutch clock it told me so,*
  And that is how I came to know.)

FLANIGAN'S FIELD

Leroy F. Jackson

Last evening the bright summer moonlight revealed
A grand jamboree out in Flanigan's Field.
The crows had a wedding, that's what I am told,
And asked all the feathers and furs, as of old.
There was Grandaddy Weasel and Billy the Bat;
There was Cocksy and Foxy and Piggy the Fat;
There were finches in yellow and sparrows in brown
And a rat in regalia, just fresh from the town;
There were snappers and flappers and quackers galore
And some of the crawlers from down on the shore.
The gander was giddy, the gopher was gay
And danced till he wore all his toenails away.
The peacock coquetted, the guinea hen smiled;
When he asked her to tango she simply went wild.
The tortoise attempted to dance with a squirrel.
The rabbit ran off with the gold-hammer girl.
But it all ended up a horrible spat
When the porcupine started to cuddle the cat.

JOHNNY FIFE AND JOHNNY'S WIFE
Mildred Plew Meigs

Oh, Johnny Fife and Johnny's wife,
  To save their toes and heels,
They built themselves a little house
  That ran on rolling wheels.

They hung their parrot at the door
  Upon a painted ring,
And round and round the world they went
  And never missed a thing;

And when they wished to eat they ate,
  And after they had fed,
They crawled beneath a crazy quilt
  And gayly went to bed;

And what they cared to keep they kept,
  And what they both did not,
They poked beneath a picket fence
  And quietly forgot.

Oh, Johnny Fife and Johnny's wife,
  They took their brush and comb,
And round and round the world they went
  And also stayed at home.

CAN A MOUSE KEEP HOUSE?

Rowena Bennett

Can a mouse
Keep house
In a skirt
And a blouse
And a little red bandanna
Just for dusting the piano,
And a little faggot broom
Just for sweeping up the room?
Can a mouse work
Well at housework?
With a thimble for a pail
And a scrub brush on her tail
Can a mouse
Keep house?

THE MELANCHOLY PIG

Lewis Carroll

There was a Pig, that sat alone,
  beside a ruined Pump.
By day and night he made his moan;
It would have stirred a heart of stone
To see him wring his hoofs and groan,
  because he could not jump.

HANNIBAL, THE CANNIBAL

Rowena Bennett

There once was a cannibal
Whose name was Hannibal.
He looked like an animal
　With rings in his nose.
He didn't wear safety pins,
He didn't wear buttons,
He didn't wear zippers
　'Cause he didn't wear clothes.
He'd never heard of smocking
And he couldn't darn a stocking,
But this wasn't very shocking
　'Cause he hadn't any hose.

The only thing he wore
Which he never ripped or tore
Was a little skirt of reeds
And a string of dangling beads
　From a most peculiar pod . . .
And there came to my attention
Other things I'd best not mention
Making Hannibal, the cannibal,
　Seem very, very odd.

224

mister mckee

JAWBREAKERS

Eunice and Janet Tietjens

D IS FOR DIPLODOCUS

D is for Diplodocus
  The biggest creature ever.
You never saw so odd a cuss,
  No, never!

For eighty feet and two he was;
  More stupid than the chickens;
And if he stepped on you, it was
  The dickens!

I IS FOR ICHTHYOSAURUS

I is for Ichthyosaurus.
  The picture shows her leading
A brood of Ichthys by her side.
Undoubtedly the artist tried
  To show the family feeding.

And when the little Ichthys grew
  To be their mother's size,
They each possessed two hundred teeth
  And huge, expressive eyes.

225

THERE ONCE WAS A PUFFIN

Florence Page Jaques

Oh, there once was a Puffin
Just the shape of a muffin,
And he lived on an island
In the
    bright
        blue sea!
He ate little fishes,
That were most delicious,
And he had them for supper
And he
    had
        them
            for tea.
But this poor little Puffin,
He couldn't play nothin',
For he hadn't anybody
To
    play
        with
            at all.
So he sat on his island,
And he cried for awhile, and
He felt very lonely,
And he
    felt
        very small.

226

Then along came the fishes,
And they said, "If you wishes,
You can have us for playmates,
Instead
    of
       for
          tea!"
So they now play together,
In all sorts of weather,
And the Puffin eàts pancakes,
Like you
    and
       like
          me.

THE ICHTHYOSAURUS

Author Unknown

There once was an Ichthyosaurus,
Who lived when the earth was all porous,
    But he fainted with shame
    When he first heard his name,
And departed a long time before us.

THE ARISTOCRAT

Carl S. Junge

Sighed Mrs. Van Cortland Chinchilla,
Ensconsed in her stylish new villa,
    "Just serve me a sherbet,
    I'm dieting, Herbert,
And flavor it, please, with vanilla."

THE KUDU

Clara E. Randall

If you've ever seen a kudu
You are lucky as so few do.
Though furred he seems to like it hot,
And roams the land of the Hottentot.

227

THE CAMEL AND THE CACHALOT
Laurence McKinney

Pherdinand the Camel, he
  Was weeping with emotion,
Though of a landed family
  He hungered for the ocean.
The Ship of the Desert,
  They christened Pherdinand,
Which maddened him exceedingly.
"May I remark," suggested he,
"A ship should sail upon the sea—
  And not upon the land."

Now Christopher the Cachalot
  (That's just a kind of whale)
Around the sea he'd dash a lot
  And all to no avail.
He looked at all the continents
  But life was dull and chill.
"You know," he said, with angry swishes,
Addressing all the little fishes,
"That one of my sincerest wishes
  Is just—to climb a hill."

228

So Pherdie found a sailor
  And sent a note to Chris,
"Let's buy ourselves a trailer
  And work the thing like this:
We'll pump up all the tires
  To float upon the sea.
It isn't much to understand,
I'll pull you when we're on the land,
But floating, on the other hand,
  You will be pulling *me*."

They sailed the whole equator
  With Pherdie in command,
But Chris was navigator
  When traveling by land;
And all the other creatures
  Are talking of them still
(Each watched of course behind a tree).
And they went down in history,
The Camel who had sailed the sea
  The Whale who climbed a hill.

PIRATE DON DURK OF DOWDEE

Mildred Plew Meigs

Ho, for the Pirate Don Durk of Dowdee!
He was as wicked as wicked could be,
But oh, he was perfectly gorgeous to see!
  The Pirate Don Durk of Dowdee.

His conscience, of course, was as black as a bat,
But he had a floppety plume on his hat
And when he went walking it jiggled—like that!
  The plume of the Pirate Dowdee.

His coat it was velvet and cut with a slash,
And often as ever he twirled his mustache
Deep down in the ocean the mermaids went splash,
  Because of Don Durk of Dowdee.

Moreover, Dowdee had a purple tattoo,
And stuck in his belt where he buckled it through
Were a dagger, a dirk, and a squizzamaroo,
   For fierce was the Pirate Dowdee.

So fearful he was he would shoot at a puff,
And always at sea when the weather grew rough
He drank from a bottle and wrote on his cuff,
   Did Pirate Don Durk of Dowdee.

Oh, he had a cutlass that swung at his thigh
And he had a parrot called Pepperkin Pye,
And a zigzaggy scar at the end of his eye
   Had Pirate Don Durk of Dowdee.

He kept in a cavern, this buccaneer bold,
A curious chest that was covered with mold,
And all of his pockets were jingly with gold!
   Oh jing! went the gold of Dowdee.

His conscience, of course, it was crook'd like a squash,
But both of his boots made a slickery slosh,
And he went through the world with a wonderful swash,
   Did Pirate Don Durk of Dowdee.

It's true he was wicked as wicked could be,
His sins they outnumbered a hundred and three,
But oh, he was perfectly gorgeous to see,
   The Pirate Don Durk of Dowdee.

THE OWL AND THE PUSSY CAT

Edward Lear

The Owl and the Pussy Cat went to sea
In a beautiful pea-green boat,
They took some honey, and plenty of money,
Wrapped up in a five-pound note.
The Owl looked up to the stars above,
And sang to a small guitar,
"O lovely Pussy! O Pussy, my love,
What a beautiful Pussy you are,
            You are,
            You are!
What a beautiful Pussy you are!"

Pussy said to the Owl, "You elegant fowl!
How charmingly sweet you sing!
O let us be married! too long we have tarried:
But what shall we do for a ring?"
They sailed away for a year and a day,
To the land where the Bong-tree grows,
And there in a wood a Piggy-wig stood,
With a ring at the end of his nose,
      His nose,
      His nose,
With a ring at the end of his nose.

"Dear Pig, are you willing to sell for one shilling
Your ring?" Said the Piggy, "I will."
So they took it away, and were married next day
By the Turkey who lives on the hill.
They dined on mince, and slices of quince,
Which they ate with a runcible spoon;
And hand in hand, on the edge of the sand,
They danced by the light of the moon,
      The moon,
      The moon,
They danced by the light of the moon.

LITTLE JOHN BOTTLEJOHN

Laura E. Richards

Little John Bottlejohn lived on the hill,
  And a blithe little man was he.
And he won the heart of a pretty mermaid
  Who lived in the deep blue sea.
And every evening she used to sit
  And sing on the rocks by the sea,
"Oh! little John Bottlejohn, pretty John Bottlejohn,
  Won't you come out to me?"

Little John Bottlejohn heard her song,
  And he opened his little door.
And he hopped and he skipped, and he skipped
    and he hopped,
  Until he came down to the shore.
And there on the rocks sat the little mermaid,
  And still she was singing so free,
"Oh! little John Bottlejohn, pretty John Bottlejohn,
  Won't you come out to me?"

Little John Bottlejohn made a bow,
  And the mermaid, she made one too,
And she said, "Oh! I never saw any one half
  So perfectly sweet as you!
In my lovely home 'neath the ocean foam,
  How happy we both might be!
Oh! little John Bottlejohn, pretty John Bottlejohn,
  Won't you come down with me?"

Little John Bottlejohn said, "Oh yes!
  I'll willingly go with you.
And I never shall quail at the sight of your tail,
  For perhaps I may grow one too."
So he took her hand, and he left the land,
  And plunged in the foaming main.
And little John Bottlejohn, pretty John Bottlejohn,
  Never was seen again.

mister mckee

THE ZANY ZOO

John Manning

THE NEIGHBORLY GNU

There once was a neighborly Gnu,
Who gossiped from ten until two
    With her new friend the Newt,
    Who was nimble and cute,
But who never knew news the Gnu knew.

THE PLAYFUL PUMA

There once was a playful young Puma,
Who pounced on a panther in Yuma,
    Who hurled him a hiss
    And biffed him like this,
Till he landed in old Montezuma.

THE TICKLY OSTRICH

An Ostrich ogled a Duck,
Who her feathers attempted to pluck;
    Her feathers were prickly,
    And as she was tickly
She kicked him to Keokuk!

THE ODOROUS OWL

An Owl who was shy and demure,
Liked to hide in a wood or a moor,
  Till he met a young Skunk,
  Who had plenty of spunk.
Now the Owl is no longer obscure.

THE TYRANNICAL TOAD

There was once a tyrannical Toad,
Who tried to own *all* of the road,
  Till he had a spat
  With a corpulent Cat
And departed with legs that were bowed.

THE TURBULENT TIGER

A Turbulent Tiger named Mabel
Was sure that her tonsils were able
    To sing on TV;
    So yowled, "Tooodleeee!"
And broke the coaxial cable.

BENJAMIN JONES AND HIS DOGS
Aileen Fisher

Benjamin Jones had a puppy named Bones,
And he taught him some tricks he could do.
Then Ben said, "If *one* little pup is such fun,
A person should really have *two*."

So Benjamin went with well nigh his last cent
And purchased a black and brown pup.
He taught him to beg, and wiggle one leg,
And dance with his ears standing up.

Then Benjamin thought, "Why, everyone ought
To have several dogs—at least *three*."
But his wife, when she heard that he wanted a third,
Exclaimed, "That sounds silly to me. . . .

"It's hard enough now to make ends meet, so how
Can we feed several dogs plus ourselves?"
But Benjy said, "Hon, these pups are such fun
They make up for bare cupboard shelves."

Well, Benjamin's purse from bad went to worse,
For he bought other puppies galore,
Until, in despair, his wife cried, "Ben, where
Can we possibly put any more?"

So Benjamin went and put up a tent
With a sign: PUPPY CIRCUS . . . and then
For the charge of a dime he ran shows all the time,
And the Joneses are eating again!

238

BENJY GOES TO THE CIRCUS

Aileen Fisher

Benjamin Jones in rollicking tones
Told his wife, "There's a circus in town.
Let's hurry and go." But his wife answered, "No.
Don't act like a silly old clown. . . .

"We've sweeping to do, and housecleaning, too.
Come, put on this dust-cap and smock,
And, provided you're good and perform as you should,
We can go at 2:30 o'clock."

Ben swept with a vim most unnatural to him.
He dusted in jittery haste.
Then he cried, "We'll be late," and dashed for the gate,
Dragging poor Mrs. Jones by the waist.

She panted, "But, but . . . your costume, tut! tut!
Your dust-cap and smock look so strange."
But, racing ahead to the circus, Ben said,
"I hadn't a moment to change."

When they got there at last, Ben's wife was aghast:
His dust-cap was over one eye.
And laughter so loud went up from the crowd
The manager rushed to see why.

He grasped Benjy's hand. He chuckled, "You're grand.
Come, be my new clown, in that dress."
And Mrs. Jones blushed, and looked rather crushed,
. . . While Ben was a howling success!

239

FATHER WILLIAM
Lewis Carroll

"You are old, Father William," the young man said,
  "And your hair has become very white;
And yet you incessantly stand on your head—
  Do you think, at your age, it is right?"

"In my youth," Father William replied to his son,
  "I feared it might injure the brain;
But, now that I'm perfectly sure I have none,
  Why, I do it again and again."

"You are old," said the youth, "as I mentioned before,
  And have grown most uncommonly fat;
Yet you turn a back-somersault in at the door—
  Pray, what is the reason of that?"

"In my youth," said the sage, as he shook his gray locks,
  "I kept all my limbs very supple
By the use of this ointment—one shilling the box—
  Allow me to sell you a couple?"

"You are old," said the youth, "and your jaws are too weak
　For anything tougher than suet;
Yet you finished the goose, with the bones and the beak—
　Pray, how did you manage to do it?"

"In my youth," said his father, "I took to the law,
　And argued each case with my wife;
And the muscular strength which it gave to my jaw
　Has lasted the rest of my life."

"You are old," said the youth, "one would hardly suppose
　That your eye was as steady as ever;
Yet you balanced an eel on the end of your nose—
　What made you so awfully clever?"

"I have answered three questions, and that is enough,"
　Said his father. "Don't give yourself airs!
Do you think I can listen all day to such stuff?
　Be off, or I'll kick you downstairs!"

THE PALE PINK TEA
Ruth Dixon

A perky little parrot on a cozy candy isle
Once planned to give a pale pink tea in just the latest style,

So issued invitations to a shy and shaky whale
Who hid behind a tiger with a temperamental tail,

And asked a Bunny Button-Eyes, a floppy clown or two,
A dinky little donkey and a denim kangaroo,

A duck with dizzy eyelids and a waddle in his walk,
A rooster with a ribbon and a high soprano squawk;

And she invited old Suzanne, a ruffled, ragged wreck,
A jiggily giraffe who wore a solid rubber neck,

And Tim, a wooden soldier with a very varnished glance
And pretty purple patches on his bird's-eye-maple pants.

But when the day was Thursday and the time was half-past three,
Not one came to the candy isle to Polly's pale pink tea.

Then Polly recollected with a fussy flannel frown
That *every* invitation was written—

UPSIDE DOWN!

EVER SEE A RHEA?
Carl S. Junge

In Patagonia, I have heard
If you're alert you're apt to see-a
Very large and graceful bird
That's known by the name of Rhea.
Don't let it see you first, beware!
Lest when you look it won't be there.

Its plumage is quite drab and gray,
At sight of it no damsel gushes.

242

Quite frankly, all that one can say
Is that it makes fine dusting brushes.
And now a word about the male
In this most Rhealistic tale.

At home he stays and sits on eggs
While over the vast pampas plain
His wives cavort and stretch their legs,
Yet he, their spouse, does not complain.
Like tired business men, no doubt
He'd rather sit than gad about.

THE UNFORTUNATE GIRAFFE
Oliver Herford

There was once a giraffe who said, "What
Do I want with my tea strong or hot?
    For my throat's such a length
    The tea loses its strength
And is cold when it reaches the spot."

CATCH ME CADDY
Leroy F. Jackson

A flying flag and a broomstick nag,
Catch me Caddy with a wingo,
Round the ring with a swing, swang, swing,
Catch me Caddy with a wingo.
We're off for the land of the Turn-Me-Round
Where the coffee's peeled and the squash is ground
And the king gets mad when the queen's around,
Catch me Caddy with a wingo.
Stand in line while the spielers shout,
Six come in while the six go out,
And you can't tell what it's all about,
So round the ring with a swing, swang, swing,
Catch me Caddy with a wingo.

THE DUCK AND THE KANGAROO

Edward Lear

Said the Duck to the Kangaroo,
  "Good gracious! how you hop
Over the fields, and the water too,
  As if you never would stop!
My life is a bore in this nasty pond:
And I long to go out in the world beyond:
  I wish I could hop like you."
  Said the Duck to the Kangaroo.

"Please give me a ride on your back,"
  Said the Duck to the Kangaroo:
"I would sit quite still, and say nothing but 'Quack'
  The whole of the long day through:
And we'd go to the Dee, and the Jelly Bo Lee,
Over the land, and over the sea:
  Please take me a ride! oh, do!"
  Said the Duck to the Kangaroo.

244

Said the Kangaroo to the Duck,
  "This requires some little reflection.
Perhaps, on the whole, it might bring me luck;
  And there seems but one objection;
Which is, if you'll let me speak so bold,
Your feet are unpleasantly wet and cold,
  And would probably give me the roo-
  Matiz," said the Kangaroo.

Said the Duck, "As I sat on the rocks,
  I have thought over that completely;
And I bought four pairs of worsted socks,
  Which fit my web-feet neatly;
And, to keep out the cold, I've bought a cloak,
And every day a cigar I'll smoke;
  All to follow my own dear true
  Love of a Kangaroo."

Said the Kangaroo, "I'm ready,
  All in the moonlight pale;
But to balance me well, dear Duck, sit steady,
  And quite at the end of my tail."
So away they went with a hop and a bound;
And they hopped the whole world three times round.
  And who so happy, oh! who,
  As the Duck and the Kangaroo.

MORE ABOUT JONATHAN BING

Beatrice Curtis Brown

"Why do you sit by yourself in the sun,
  Jonathan Bing, Jonathan Bing?
Why do you sit by yourself in the sun,
When you know there is plenty of work
    to be done,
  Jonathan, Jonathan Bing?"

"Why, do you ask, by myself do I sit?"
  Said Jonathan Bing, Jonathan Bing.
"The question is foolish, as you must admit,
For there's no one, I think, that can *help*
    you to sit,"
  Said Jonathan, Jonathan Bing.

"Why do you sit on the floor, if you please,
  Jonathan Bing, Jonathan Bing?
Why do you sit on the floor, if you please,
Holding a dining-room chair on your knees,
  Jonathan, Jonathan Bing?"

"For sixty odd years, without any mishap,"
  Said Jonathan Bing, Jonathan Bing,
"This chair has supported my weight on its lap,
Now it's sitting on me while it takes a short nap,"
  Said Jonathan, Jonathan Bing.

"What are you making that racket about,
  Jonathan Bing, Jonathan Bing?
What are you chipping and chopping about,
Why are you taking that staircase out,
  Jonathan, Jonathan Bing?"

"I'm turning it up so it stands on its head,"
  Said Jonathan Bing, Jonathan Bing,
"So the stairs will go down when I go up to bed,
And if they go *up* when I come *down*, instead,
  What matter?" said Jonathan Bing.

246

A NEW SONG TO SING ABOUT JONATHAN BING

Beatrice Curtis Brown

O Jonathan Bing, O Bingathon Jon!
Forgets where he's going and thinks he has gone.
He wears his false teeth on the top of his head,
And always stands up when he's sleeping in bed.

O Jonathan Bing has a curious way
Of trying to walk into yesterday,
"If I end with my breakfast and start with my tea,
I *ought* to be able to do it," says he.

O Jonathan Bing is a miser, they say,
For he likes to save trouble and put it away.
"If I never get up in the morning," he said,
"I shall save all the trouble of going to bed!"

"O Jonathan Bing! What a way to behave!
And what do you do with the trouble you save?"
"I wrap it up neatly and send it by post
To my friends and relations who need it the most

Part VII: IN LULLABY LAND

LADY BUTTON–EYES
Eugene Field

When the busy day is done,
And my weary little one
Rocketh gently to and fro,
When the night winds softly blow,
And the crickets in the glen
Chirp and chirp and chirp again,
When upon the haunted green
Fairies dance around their queen—
Then from yonder misty skies
Cometh Lady Button-Eyes.

Through the murk and mist and gloom
To our quiet cozy home,
Where to singing, sweet and low,
Rocks a cradle to and fro
Where the clock's dull monotone
Telleth of the day that's done;
Where the moonbeams hover o'er
Playthings sleeping on the floor—
Where my weary wee one lies
Cometh Lady Button-Eyes.

Cometh like a fleeting ghost
From some distant eerie coast;
Never footfall can you hear
As that spirit fareth near—
Never whisper, never word
From that shadow-queen is heard.
In ethereal raiment dight,
From the realm of fay and sprite
In the depth of yonder skies
Cometh Lady Button-Eyes.

Layeth she her hands upon
My dear weary little one,
And those white hands overspread
Like a veil the curly head
Seem to fondle and caress
Every little silken tress;
Then she smooths the eyelids down
Over those two eyes of brown—
In such soothing, tender wise
Cometh Lady Button-Eyes.

Dearest, feel upon your brow
That caressing magic now;
For the crickets in the glen
Chirp and chirp and chirp again,
While upon the haunted green
Fairies dance around their queen,
And the moonbeams hover o'er
Playthings sleeping on the floor—
Hush, my sweet! From yonder skies
Cometh Lady Button-Eyes!

249

MOON SONG

Mildred Plew Meigs

Zoon, zoon, cuddle and croon—
    Over the crinkling sea,
The moon man flings him a silvered net
    Fashioned of moonbeams three.

And some folks say when the net lies long
    And the midnight hour is ripe;
The moon man fishes for some old song
    That fell from a sailor's pipe.

And some folk say that he fishes the bars
    Down where the dead ships lie,
Looking for lost little baby stars
    That slid from the slippery sky.

And the waves roll out and the waves roll in
    And the nodding night wind blows,
But why the moon man fishes the sea
    Only the moon man knows.

Zoon, zoon, net of the moon
    Rides on the wrinkling sea;
Bright is the fret and shining wet,
    Fashioned of moonbeams three.

And some folk say when the great net gleams
    And the waves are dusky blue,
The moon man fishes for two little dreams
    He lost when the world was new.

And some folk say in the late night hours
    While the long fin-shadows slide,
The moon man fishes for cold sea flowers
    Under the tumbling tide.

And the waves roll out and the waves roll in,
    And the gray gulls dip and doze,
But why the moon man fishes the sea,
    Only the moon man knows.

Zoon, zoon, cuddle and croon—
    Over the crinkling sea,
The moon man flings him a silvered net
    Fashioned of moonbeams three.

And some folk say that he follows the flecks
    Down where the last light flows,
Fishing for two round gold-rimmed "specs"
    That blew from his button-like nose.

And some folks say while the salt sea foams
    And the silver net lines snare,
The moon man fishes for carven combs
    That float from the mermaids' hair.

And the waves roll out and the waves roll in
    And the nodding night wind blows,
But why the moon man fishes the sea
    Only the moon man knows.

CRADLE SONG

Elizabeth-Ellen Long

While boys and girls lie dreaming
In cities and on farms,
The sea is rocking stars to sleep
In her old dark arms,

Rocking drowsy stars to sleep
And a tired moon, too,
With lullabies already old
When the world was new!

SONG AT DUSK

Nancy Byrd Turner

The flowers nod,
The shadows creep,
A star comes over the hill;
The youngest lamb
Has gone to sleep,
The smallest bird is still.

The world is full
Of drowsy things
And sweet with candlelight;
The nests are full
Of folded wings—
Good night, good night, good night!

252

ON OUR WAY TO DREAMLAND

Clare Joslyn

A little ship comes sailing by
    From out the sky so blue,
To take my baby riding
    And I am going, too;
The fat old moon will laugh at us
    And wink his merry eye.
He thinks it is so funny
    To see us sailing by.

In and out the stars we float,
In our little Dreamland boat,
Baby and I, hush, lullaby,
    On our way to Dreamland.

The waves are dashing overhead,
    As white, as white as snow!
We see them floating up there
    And call them clouds, you know.
They say the fishing thereabout
    For starfish is just fine;
We slip them through our fingers
    And laugh to see them shine.

In and out the stars we float
In our little Dreamland boat,
Baby and I, hush, lullaby,
    On our way to Dreamland!

THE HARBOR OF HUSHABY HO
Mildred Plew Meigs

When the winds wind out with a hi, ho, hum,
  At the edge of the Hushaby Sea,
And the Hushaby waves they strum and strum
  With a tender melody,

Then soft and soft while the shadows spin
  And the poppy sun swings low,
The little toy boats sail in, sail in,
  To the Harbor of Hushaby Ho.

Little toy boats that children set
  Tossing atop the sea,
Lost and weary and worn and wet
  And tired as tired can be—

One by one while the waves they strum
  And the day goes down like a sail,
The little toy boats with hi, ho, hum,
  Rock home on the Hushaby trail.

And some they limp with a frightful limp,
  And some have lost their twine,
And some have never a sail to skimp,
  And some are choked with brine;

But safe at last when the shadows spin
  And the poppy sun swings low,
The little toy boats sail in, sail in,
  To the Harbor of Hushaby Ho.

CRADLE HYMN

Martin Luther

Away in a manger, no crib for a bed,
The little Lord Jesus laid down his sweet head.
The stars in the bright sky looked down where he lay—
The little Lord Jesus asleep on the hay.
The cattle are lowing, the baby awakes,
But little Lord Jesus no crying he makes.
I love thee, Lord Jesus! look down from the sky,
And stay by my cradle till morning is nigh.

THE ROCK–A–BY LADY

Eugene Field

The Rock-a-By Lady from Hushaby street
   Comes stealing; comes creeping;
The poppies they hang from her head to her feet,
And each hath a dream that is tiny and fleet—
She bringeth her poppies to you, my sweet,
   ·When she findeth you sleeping!

There is one little dream of a beautiful drum—
   "Rub-a-dub!" it goeth;
There is one little dream of a big sugar-plum,
And lo! thick and fast the other dreams come
Of popguns that bang, and tin tops that hum,
   And a trumpet that bloweth!

And dollies peep out of those wee little dreams
   With laughter and singing;
And boats go a-floating on silvery streams,
And the stars peek-a-boo with their own misty gleams,
And up, up, and up, where the Mother Moon beams,
   The fairies go winging!

Would you dream all these dreams that are tiny and fleet?
   They'll come to you sleeping;
So shut the two eyes that are weary, my sweet,
For the Rock-a-By Lady from Hushaby street,
With poppies that hang from her head to her feet,
   Comes stealing; comes creeping.

255

SONG FOR ROBERTA
Adele Jordan Tarr

When morning sun wakes you and me,
The little birds wake in the tree,
And little boats put out to sea.

When noontime comes the sun is high,
We play together, you and I,
(You'll take a nap, though, by and by.)

And when the western sky is red,
The baby birds must go to bed,
And little boats are homeward sped.

And when at last the moon is bright,
Upon your pillow, soft and white,
Your sleepy head will rest all night.

LITTLE BLUE PIGEON
Eugene Field

Sleep, little pigeon, and fold your wings—
 Little blue pigeon with velvet eyes;
Sleep to the singing of mother-bird swinging—
 Swinging the nest where her little one lies.

Away out yonder I see a star—
 Silvery star with a tinkling song;
To the soft dew falling I hear it calling—
 Calling and tinkling the night along.

In through the window a moonbeam comes—
 Little gold moonbeam with misty wings;
All silently creeping, it asks: "Is he sleeping—
 Sleeping and dreaming while mother sings?"

. . . .

But sleep, little pigeon, and fold your wings—
 Little blue pigeon with mournful eyes;
Am I not singing?—see, I am swinging—
 Swinging the nest where my darling lies.

256

DANCER IN THE SUN

Scharmel Iris

The sun is like a ball of brass,
  The sky is like a bowl of blue.
  Your father on his flute for you
Music is making.
The rabbit in the desert grass
His ear is shaking.
  Run, little baby, run,
  Dance with the rabbit here in the sun!

The Sun is a Navajo runner in the sky
  Running a race in a desert blue;
My baskets all unfinished lie
  And your father flutes for you;
The rabbit with the dance is done,
You alone dance in the sun,
Come to your mother,
Run little dancer,
Home little dancer,
Out of the sun.

SEAL LULLABY
Rudyard Kipling

Oh! hush thee, my baby, the night is behind us,
    And black are the waters that sparkled so green.
The moon, o'er the combers, looks downward to find us
    At rest in the hollows that rustle between.
Where billow meets billow, there soft be thy pillow;
    Ah, weary wee flipperling, curl at thy ease!
The storm shall not wake thee, nor shark overtake thee,
    Asleep in the arms of the slow-swinging seas.

INDIAN SONG
Elizabeth-Ellen Long

Oh, happy day
Begun in beauty
And finished in beauty also!
When the morning was new
A meadow lark sang in the fields
Outside my village,
And at noon a cloud of white butterflies
Drifted across the sun.
Now when the smoke of evening fires
Hangs gray above the houses of my people
The Moon-Woman comes out of the hills
Driving her flock of stars before her.

FOREST LULLABY

Leona Stafford

The little bear baby is fast asleep,
  'Way back in a cave in the wood.
Little bear baby played hard all day,
  Hard as a baby bear could.
He fished in a clear little stream for fish,
  And tried to take honey from bees
Who gathered the nectar from clover fields
  To store in the hollows of trees.
The little gray squirrels are fast asleep,
  'Way up in the oak tree high,
Dreaming and swinging in cozy beds
  To the tune of a wind lullaby.

The bees are asleep on the honey comb
  And the big gnarly knots of the oak.
The frogs are asleep on the banks of the stream
  Where in daylight they frolic and croak.
But the forest still stirs in a quiet way,
  For 'possums and coons are abroad,
And the owls who use the nighttime to hunt
  And the daytime to slumber and nod.

Hush, little boy, don't make any noise,
  Lest you wake the bear baby, the bees,
And all the wood creatures who sleep tonight
  In caves and hollows of trees.
The coon is so quiet on fur-mittened feet,
  The 'possum goes silently, too,
And the owl flops his wings with a soundless swish
  As he softly calls, "Who? Who? Who?"

DREAM–SONG
Walter de la Mare

Sunlight, moonlight,
Twilight, starlight—
Gloaming at the close of day,
And an owl calling,
Cool dews falling
In a wood of oak and may.

Lantern-light, taper-light,
Torchlight, no-light:
Darkness at the shut of day,
And lions roaring,
Their wrath pouring
In wild waste places far away.

Elf-light, bat-light,
Touchwood-light and toad-light,
And the sea a shimmering gloom of gray,
And a small face smiling
In a dream's beguiling
In a world of wonders far away.

WYNKEN, BLYNKEN, AND NOD

Eugene Field

Wynken, Blynken, and Nod one night
  Sailed off in a wooden shoe—
Sailed on a river of crystal light,
  Into a sea of dew.
"Where are you going, and what do you wish?"
  The old moon asked the three.
"We have come to fish for the herring fish
  That live in this beautiful sea;
  Nets of silver and gold have we!"
      Said Wynken,
      Blynken,
      And Nod.

The old moon laughed and sang a song,
  As they rocked in the wooden shoe,
And the wind that sped them all night long
  Ruffled the waves of dew.
The little stars were the herring fish
  That lived in that beautiful sea—
"Now cast your nets wherever you wish—
  Never afeared are we";
So cried the stars to the fishermen three:
      Wynken,
      Blynken,
      And Nod.

All night long their nets they threw
  To the stars in the twinkling foam—
Then down from the skies came the wooden shoe,
  Bringing the fishermen home;
'Twas all so pretty a sail it seemed
  As if it could not be,
And some folks thought 'twas a dream they'd dreamed
  Of sailing that beautiful sea—
  But I shall name you the fishermen three:
      Wynken,
      Blynken,
      And Nod.

Wynken and Blynken are two little eyes,
  And Nod is a little head,
And the wooden shoe that sailed the skies
  Is a wee one's trundle bed.
So shut your eyes while mother sings
  Of wonderful sights that be,
And you shall see the beautiful things
  As you rock in the misty sea,
  Where the old shoe rocked the fishermen three:
    Wynken,
    Blynken,
    And Nod.

SWEET AND LOW

Alfred Tennyson

Sweet and low, sweet and low,
  Wind of the western sea!
Low, low, breathe and blow,
  Wind of the western sea!
Over the rolling waters go,
Come from the dying moon and blow,
  Blow him again to me;
While my little one, while my pretty one, sleeps.

Sleep and rest, sleep and rest,
  Father will come to thee soon;
Rest, rest, on mother's breast,
  Father will come to thee soon;
Father will come to his babe in the nest,
Silver sails all out of the west
  Under the silver moon:
Sleep, my little one, sleep, my pretty one, sleep.

WE GIVE OUR THANKS
Clara E. Randall

For making plants to grow our food,
Dear God, we give our thanks to You.
We'll show our thanks by being good,
For we are glad You made us, too!

THANK YOU, LORD
Marjorie Allen Anderson

Wrens and robins back once more;
Tulips blooming near our door;
Roller skates that zip and sing;
Colored marbles, tops, and string;
Wind that frolics, romps, and plays—
We thank you, Lord, for warm spring days.

Little boats to launch and sail;
Sand to dig with spade and pail;
Picnics spread in shady nooks;
Bare feet wading in cool brooks;
Quiet, tawny cows that graze—
We thank you, Lord, for summer days.

Juicy apples sweet and red;
Pumpkins stored out in the shed;
Harvest fragrance in the air;
Brown leaves blowing everywhere;
Bonfires with their smoky haze—
We thank you, Lord, for autumn days.

Nipping winds that whistle low;
Patterned flakes of falling snow;
Skating on the glassy lake;
Snowmen, so much fun to make;
Frozen roads with sleds and sleighs—
We thank you, Lord, for winter days.

265

IN CHURCH
Clara E. Randall

In church just when the organ plays so low,
And people bow and think a quiet prayer,
And all the painted altar windows glow,
I feel Someone we do not see is there.

CHILD'S PRAYER
Elizabeth-Ellen Long

For grass and flowers and growing trees,
For birds and butterflies and bees,
For our fathers and our mothers,
For our sisters and our brothers,
We thank You, God.

For home and all the love that's there,
For food we eat and clothes we wear,
For books to read and songs to sing,
For playmates and for everything,
We thank You, God.

Help us, please, both day and night
To do what we've been taught is right,
And let our tongues speak only good
Of others as Your children should,
Teach us to share and how to find
True happiness in being kind,
So that we never harm at all
One living creature, large or small,
And we will never night or day
Or any time forget to say
We thank You, God!

HE PRAYETH BEST
Samuel Taylor Coleridge

He prayeth best who loveth best
All things both great and small;
For the dear God who loveth us,
He made and loveth all.

266

GENTLE JESUS, MEEK AND MILD

Charles Wesley

Gentle Jesus, meek and mild,
Look upon a little child,
Pity my simplicity,
Teach me, Lord, to come to Thee.

Fain would I to Thee be brought,
Dearest Lord, forbid it not;
In the Kingdom of Thy grace
Give a little child a place.

SLEEP, BABY, SLEEP

Author Unknown

Sleep, baby, sleep!
Thy father watches the sheep;
Thy mother is shaking the dreamland tree
And down comes a little dream on thee.
Sleep, baby, sleep!

Sleep, baby, sleep!
The large stars are the sheep;
The little stars are the lambs, I guess;
And the gentle moon is the shepherdess.
Sleep, baby, sleep!

Sleep, baby, sleep!
Our Savior loves His sheep:
He is the Lamb of God on high,
Who for our sakes came down to die.
Sleep, baby, sleep!

ALL THINGS BEAUTIFUL

Cecil Francis Alexander

All things bright and beautiful,
    All creatures great and small,
All things wise and wonderful,
    The Lord God made them all.

Each little flower that opens,
    Each little bird that sings,
He made their glowing colors,
    He made their tiny wings.

The purple-headed mountain,
    The river running by,
The sunset, and the morning,
    That brighten up the sky;—

The cold wind in the winter,
    The pleasant summer sun,
The ripe fruits in the garden,
    He made them every one.

The tall trees in the greenwood,
    The meadows where we play,
The rushes by the water,
    We gather every day—

He gave us eyes to see them,
    And lips that we might tell
How great is God Almighty,
    Who has made all things well.

ALL THROUGH THE NIGHT

Author Unknown

Sleep, my babe, lie still and slumber,
    All through the night;
Guardian angels God will lend thee,
    All through the night;

Soft the drowsy hours are creeping,
Hill and vale in slumber sleeping,
Mother dear her watch is keeping,
    All through the night.

God is here, thou'lt not be lonely,
    All through the night;
'Tis not I who guards thee only,
    All through the night.
Night's dark shades will soon be over,
Still my watchful care shall hover,
God with me His watch is keeping,
    All through the night.

GOD IS LIKE THIS

Rowena Bennett

I cannot see the wind at all
    Or hold it in my hand,
And yet I know there is a wind
    Because it swirls the sand.
I know there is a wondrous wind,
    Because I glimpse its power
Whenever it bends low a tree
    Or sways the smallest flower.

And God is very much like this,
    Invisible as air;
I cannot touch or see Him, yet
    I know that He is there
Because I glimpse His wondrous works
    And goodness everywhere.

CHILD'S PRAYER FOR OTHER CHILDREN

Elizabeth-Ellen Long

Little children everywhere,
White, yellow, black or brown,
Sleeping here at home with me
Or in some foreign town,

Bless them all and keep them safe
Within Your love, dear God,
Little children everywhere,
Both here and far abroad.

You are the Father of us all,
Of them as well as me,
And black or yellow, brown or white,
We are Your family.

You are the Father of us all,
And all are in Your care,
The little children sleeping
Both here and everywhere.

THE YEAR'S AT THE SPRING
Robert Browning

The year's at the spring
And the day's at the morn;
Morning's at seven;
The hillside's dew-pearled;
The lark's on the wing;
The snail's on the thorn:
God's in his heaven—
All's right with the world!

HIE AWAY, HIE AWAY
Sir Walter Scott

Hie away, hie away,
Over bank and over brae,
Where the copsewood is the greenest,
Where the fountains glisten sheenest,
Where the lady-fern grows strongest,
Where the morning dew lies longest,
Where the black-cock sweetest sips it,
Where the fairy latest trips it:
Hie to haunts right seldom seen,
Lovely, lonesome, cool, and green,
Over bank and over brae,
Hie away, hie away.

271

HARK! HARK! THE LARK
William Shakespeare

Hark! hark! the lark at heaven's gate sings,
  And Phœbus 'gins arise,
His steeds to water at those springs
  On chaliced flowers that lies;

And winking Mary-buds begin
  To ope their golden eyes;
With every thing that pretty is,
  My lady sweet, arise;
    Arise, arise.

DAFFODILS
William Wordsworth

I wandered lonely as a cloud
That floats on high o'er vales and hills,
When all at once I saw a crowd,
A host, of golden daffodils,—
Beside the lake, beneath the trees,
Fluttering, dancing in the breeze.

Continuous as the stars that shine
And twinkle on the milky way,
They stretched in never-ending line
Along the margin of a bay:
Ten thousand saw I at a glance,
Tossing their heads in sprightly dance.

The waves beside them danced; but they
Outdid the sparkling waves in glee:
A poet could not but be gay
In such a jocund company:

I gazed, and gazed, but little thought
What wealth the show to me had brought.

For oft, when on my couch I lie
In vacant or in pensive mood,
They flash upon that inward eye
Which is the bliss of solitude;
And then my heart with pleasure fills,
And dances with the daffodils.

A SEA SONG

Allan Cunningham

A wet sheet and a flowing sea;
   A wind that follows fast,
And fills the white and rustling sail
   And bends the gallant mast;
And bends the gallant mast, my boys,
   While like the eagle free,
Away the good ship flies, and leaves
   Old England on the lee.

O for a soft and gentle wind!
   I heard a fair one cry;
But give to me the snoring breeze
   And white waves heaving high;
And white waves heaving high, my lads,
   The good ship light and free—
The world of waters is our home,
   And merry men are we.

There's tempest in yon horned moon,
   And lightning in yon cloud;
But hark the music, mariners!
   The wind is piping loud;
The wind is piping loud, my boys,
   The lightning flashes free—
While the hollow oak our palace is,
   Our heritage the sea.

HOME–THOUGHTS, FROM ABROAD
Robert Browning

Oh, to be in England
  Now that April's there,
And whoever wakes in England
  Sees, some morning, unaware,
That the lowest boughs and the brush-wood sheaf
Round the elm-tree bole are in tiny leaf,
While the chaffinch sings on the orchard bough
In England—now!

And after April, when May follows,
And the whitethroat builds, and all the swallows!
Hark, where my blossomed pear tree in the hedge
  Leans to the field and scatters on the clover
Blossoms and dewdrops—at the bent spray's edge—
  That's the wise thrush; he sings each song twice over,
Lest you should think he never could recapture
The first fine careless rapture!
And though the fields look rough with hoary dew,
All will be gay when noontide wakes anew
The buttercups, the little children's dower
—Far brighter than this gaudy melon-flower!

From THE VISION OF SIR LAUNFAL
James Russell Lowell

And what is so rare as a day in June?
  Then, if ever, come perfect days;
Then Heaven tries the earth if it be in tune,
  And over it softly her warm ear lays.
Whether we look, or whether we listen,
We hear life murmur, or see it glisten;
Every clod feels a stir of might,
  An instinct within it that reaches and towers,
And, groping blindly above it for light,
  Climbs to a soul in grass and flowers;
The flush of life may well be seen
  Thrilling back over hills and valleys;
The cowslip startles in meadows green,

The buttercup catches the sun in its chalice,
And there's never a leaf nor a blade too mean
  To be some happy creature's palace;
The little bird sits at his door in the sun,
  Atilt like a blossom among the leaves,
And lets his illumined being o'errun
  With the deluge of summer it receives;
His mate feels the eggs beneath her wings,
And the heart in her dumb breast flutters and sings;
He sings to the wide world, and she to her nest,—
In the nice ear of Nature which song is the best?

WHO HAS SEEN THE WIND?
Christina Rossetti

Who has seen the wind?
  Neither I nor you:
But when the leaves hang trembling,
  The wind is passing through.

Who has seen the wind?
  Neither you nor I:
But when the trees bow down their heads,
  The wind is passing by.

THERE WAS A ROARING IN THE WIND
William Wordsworth

There was a roaring in the wind all night;
The rain came heavily and fell in floods;
But now the sun is rising calm and bright;
The birds are singing in the distant woods;
Over his own sweet voice the Stock-dove broods;
The Jay makes answer as the Magpie chatters;
And all the air is filled with pleasant noise of waters.

All things that love the sun are out of doors;
The sky rejoices in the morning's birth;
The grass is bright with raindrops;—on the moors
The hare is running races in her mirth;
And with her feet she from the plashy earth
Raises a mist, that, glittering in the sun,
Runs with her all the way, wherever she doth run.

UPON WESTMINSTER BRIDGE
William Wordsworth

Earth has not anything to show more fair:
Dull would he be of soul who could pass by
A sight so touching in its majesty:
This City now doth, like a garment, wear
The beauty of the morning; silent, bare,
Ships, towers, domes, theaters, and temples lie
Open unto the fields, and to the sky;
All bright and glittering in the smokeless air.

Never did sun more beautifully steep
In his first splendor, valley, rock, or hill;
Ne'er saw I, never felt, a calm so deep!
The river glideth at his own sweet will:
Dear God! the very houses seem asleep;
And all that mighty heart is lying still!

THE RHODORA
Ralph Waldo Emerson

In May, when sea-winds pierced our solitudes,
I found the fresh Rhodora in the woods,
Spreading its leafless blooms in a damp nook,
To please the desert and the sluggish brook.
The purple petals, fallen in the pool,
Made the black water with their beauty gay;
Here might the redbird come his plumes to cool,
And court the flower that cheapens his array.

Rhodora! if the sages ask thee why
This charm is wasted on the earth and sky,
Tell them, dear, that if eyes were made for seeing,
Then Beauty is its own excuse for being:
Why thou were there, O rival of the rose!
I never thought to ask, I never knew:
But, in my simple ignorance, suppose
The self-same Power that brought me there brought you.

276

THE CRIMSON DAWN
Percy Bysshe Shelley

The point of one white star is quivering still
Deep in the orange light of widening morn
Beyond the purple mountains: thro' a chasm
Of wind-divided mist the darker lake
Reflects it: now it wanes: it gleams again
As the waves fade, and as the burning threads
Of woven cloud unravel in pale air:
'Tis lost! and thro' yon peaks of cloudlike snow
The roseate sunlight quivers: hear I not
The Aeolian music of her sea-green plumes
Winnowing the crimson dawn?

YE STARS
Lord Byron

Ye stars! which are the poetry of heaven!
If in your bright leaves we would read the fate
Of men and empires,—'tis to be forgiven,
That in our aspirations to be great,
Our destinies o'erleap their mortal state,
And claim a kindred with you; for ye are
A beauty and a mystery, and create
In us such love and reverence from afar,
That fortune, fame, power, life, have named
　　themselves a star.

DEAR LAND OF ALL MY LOVE
Sidney Lanier

Long as thine Art shall love true love,
Long as thy Science truth shall know,
Long as thine Eagle harms no Dove,
Long as thy Law by law shall grow,
Long as thy God is God above,
Thy brother every man below,
So long, dear Land of all my love,
Thy name shall shine, thy fame shall glow!

277

CANADIAN BOAT-SONG

Thomas Moore

Faintly as tolls the evening chime
Our voices keep tune and our oars keep time.
Soon as the woods on the shore look dim,
We'll sing at St. Ann's our parting hymn,
Row, brothers, row, the stream runs fast,
The rapids are near and the daylight's past.

Why should we yet our sail unfurl?
There is not a breath the blue wave to curl,
But, when the wind blows off the shore,
Oh, sweetly we'll rest our weary oar.
Blow, breezes, blow, the stream runs fast,
The rapids are near and the daylight's past.

Utawas' tide! this trembling moon
Shall see us float over thy surges soon.
Saint of this green isle! hear our prayers, ·
Oh, grant us cool heavens and favoring airs.
Blow, breezes, blow, the stream runs fast,
The rapids are near and the daylight's past.

SWEET AFTON

Robert Burns

Flow gently, sweet Afton! among thy green braes,
Flow gently, I'll sing thee a song in thy praise;
My Mary's asleep by thy murmuring stream,
Flow gently, sweet Afton, disturb not her dream.

Thou stock-dove whose echo resounds thro' the glen,
Ye wild whistling blackbirds in yon thorny den,
Thou green crested lapwing, thy screaming forbear,
I charge you, disturb not my slumbering Fair.

How lofty, sweet Afton, thy neighboring hills,
Far mark'd with the courses of clear, winding rills;
There daily I wander as noon rises high,
My flocks and my Mary's sweet cot in my eye.

How pleasant thy banks and green valleys below,
Where, wild in the woodlands, the primroses blow;
There oft, as mild ev'ning weeps over the lea,
The sweet-scented birk shades my Mary and me.

Thy crystal stream, Afton, how lovely it glides,
And winds by the cot where my Mary resides;
How wanton thy waters her snowy feet lave,
As, gathering sweet flowerets, she stems thy clear wave.

Flow gently, sweet Afton, among thy green braes,
Flow gently, sweet river, the theme of my lays;
My Mary's asleep by thy murmuring stream,
Flow gently, sweet Afton, disturb not her dream.

THE OWL

Alfred Tennyson

When cats run home and light is come,
    And dew is cold upon the ground,
And the far-off stream is dumb,
    And the whirring sail goes round,
    And the whirring sail goes round;
      Alone and warming his five wits,
      The white owl in the belfry sits.

When merry milkmaids click the latch,
    And rarely smells the new-mown hay,
And the cock hath sung beneath the thatch
    Twice or thrice his roundelay,
    Twice or thrice his roundelay;
      Alone and warming his five wits,
      The white owl in the belfry sits.

THE SOLITARY REAPER
William Wordsworth

Behold her, single in the field,
Yon solitary Highland Lass!
Reaping and singing by herself;
Stop here, or gently pass!

Alone she cuts and binds the grain,
And sings a melancholy strain;
O listen! for the Vale profound
Is overflowing with the sound.

No Nightingale did ever chant
More welcome notes to weary bands
Of travelers in some shady haunt,
Among Arabian sands:

A voice so thrilling ne'er was heard
In springtime from the Cuckoo-bird,
Breaking the silence of the seas
Among the farthest Hebrides.

Will no one tell me what she sings?—
Perhaps the plaintive numbers flow
For old, unhappy, far-off things,
And battles long ago:

Or is it some more humble lay,
Familiar matter of today?
Some natural sorrow, loss, or pain,
That has been, and may be again?

Whate'er the theme, the maiden sang
As if her song could have no ending;
I saw her singing at her work,
And o'er the sickle bending;—

I listened, motionless and still;
And, as I mounted up the hill,
The music in my ear I bore
Long after it was heard no more.

BREATHES THERE THE MAN WITH SOUL SO DEAD

Sir Walter Scott

Breathes there the man with soul so dead
Who never to himself hath said,
This is my own, my native land!
Whose heart hath ne'er within him burned,
As home his footsteps he hath turned
From wandering on a foreign strand?
If such there breathe, go, mark him well;
For him no minstrel raptures swell;
High though his titles, proud his name,
Boundless his wealth as wish can claim,
Despite those titles, power, and pelf,
The wretch, concentered all in self,
Living, shall forfeit fair renown,
And, doubly dying, shall go down
To the vile dust from whence he sprung,
Unwept, unhonored, and unsung.

I HEAR AMERICA SINGING

Walt Whitman

I hear America singing, the varied carols I hear,
Those of mechanics, each one singing his as it should be, blithe and
strong,
The carpenter singing his as he measures his plank or beam,
The mason singing as he makes ready for work, or leaves off work,
The boatman singing what belongs to him in the boat, the deck-
hand singing on the steamboat deck,
The shoemaker singing as he sits on his bench, the hatter singing as
he stands,
The woodcutter's song, the ploughboy's on his way in the morning,
or at noon intermission, or at sundown,
The delicious singing of the mother, or of the young wife at work,
or of the girl singing or washing,
Each singing what belongs to him or her and to none else,
The day that belongs to the day—at night the party of young fel-
lows, robust, friendly,
Singing with open mouths their strong, melodious songs.

BALLAD OF THE OYSTERMAN

Oliver Wendell Holmes

It was a tall young oysterman lived by the riverside,
His shop was just upon the bank, his boat was on the tide;
The daughter of a fisherman, that was so straight and slim,
Lived over on the other bank, right opposite to him.
It was the pensive oysterman that saw a lovely maid,
Upon a moonlight evening, a-sitting in the shade;
He saw her wave her handkerchief, as much as if to say,
"I'm wide awake, young oysterman, and all the folks away."

Then up arose the oysterman, and to himself said he,
"I guess I'll leave the skiff at home, for fear that folks should see;
I read it in the story-book, that, for to kiss his dear,
Leander swam the Hellespont,—and I will swim this here."
And he has leaped into the waves, and crossed the shining stream,
And he has clambered up the bank, all in the moonlight gleam;

Frances
Eckart

O there were kisses sweet as dew, and words as soft as rain,—
But they have heard her father's step, and in he leaps again!

Out spoke the ancient fisherman,—"O what was that, my daughter?"
" 'T was nothing but a pebble, sir, I threw into the water."
"And what is that, pray tell me, love, that paddles off so fast?"
"It's nothing but a porpoise, sir, that's been a swimming past."
Out spoke the ancient fisherman,—"Now bring me my harpoon!
I'll get into my fishing-boat, and fix the fellow soon."
Down fell that pretty innocent, as falls a snow-white lamb,
Her hair drooped round her pallid cheeks, like seaweed on a clam.

Alas for those two loving ones! she waked not from her swound,
And he was taken with the cramp, and in the waves was drowned;
But Fate has metamorphosed them, in pity of their woe,
And now they keep an oyster-shop for mermaids down below.

THE BELLS

Edgar Allan Poe

Hear the sledges with the bells—
    Silver bells!
What a world of merriment their melody foretells!
    How they tinkle, tinkle, tinkle,
      In the icy air of night!
    While the stars that oversprinkle
    All the heavens, seem to twinkle
      With a crystalline delight;
    Keeping time, time, time,
    In a sort of Runic rhyme,
  To the tintinnabulation that so musically wells
    From the bells, bells, bells, bells,
      Bells, bells, bells—
From the jingling and the tinkling of the bells.

    Hear the mellow wedding bells—
      Golden bells!
What a world of happiness their harmony foretells!
    Through the balmy air of night
    How they ring out their delight!—
    From the molten-golden notes,
      And all in tune,
    What a liquid ditty floats
To the turtle-dove that listens, while she gloats
      On the moon!
    Oh, from out the sounding cells,
What a gush of euphony voluminously wells!
      How it swells!
      How it dwells
    On the Future!—how it tells
    Of the rapture that impels
    To the swinging and the ringing
      Of the bells, bells, bells—
    Of the bells, bells, bells, bells,
      Bells, bells, bells—
To the rhyming and the chiming of the bells!

Hear the loud alarum bells—
Brazen bells!
What a tale of terror, now their turbulency tells!
In the startled ear of night
How they scream out their affright!
Too much horrified to speak,
They can only shriek, shriek,
Out of tune,
In a clamorous appealing to the mercy of the fire,
In a mad expostulation with the deaf and frantic fire,
Leaping higher, higher, higher,
With a desperate desire,
And a resolute endeavor
Now—now to sit, or never,
By the side of the pale-faced moon.
Oh, the bells, bells, bells!
What a tale their terror tells
Of Despair!
How they clang, and clash, and roar!
What a horror they outpour
On the bosom of the palpitating air!
Yet the ear, it fully knows,
By the twanging,
And the clanging,
How the danger ebbs and flows;
Yet the ear distinctly tells,
In the jangling,
And the wrangling,
How the danger sinks and swells,
By the sinking or the swelling in the anger of the bells—
Of the bells—
Of the bells, bells, bells, bells,
Bells, bells, bells—
In the clamor and the clanging of the bells!

Hear the tolling of the bells—
Iron bells!
What a world of solemn thought their monody compels!

285

In the silence of the night,
  How we shiver with affright
At the melancholy menace of their tone!
  For every sound that floats
  From the rust within their throats
    Is a groan.
  And the people—ah, the people—
  They that dwell up in the steeple,
    All alone,
  And who, tolling, tolling, tolling,
  In that muffled monotone,
  Feel a glory in so rolling
  On the human heart a stone—
They are neither man nor woman—
They are neither brute nor human—
    They are Ghouls:—
  And their king it is who tolls:—
  And he rolls, rolls, rolls,
    Rolls
  A paean from the bells!
  And his merry bosom swells
  With the paean of the bells!
  And he dances, and he yells;
  Keeping time, time, time,
  In a sort of Runic rhyme,
  To the paean of the bells:—
    Of the bells:
  Keeping time, time, time,
  In a sort of Runic rhyme,
  To the throbbing of the bells:—
  Of the bells, bells, bells—
  To the sobbing of the bells:—
  Keeping time, time, time,
  As he knells, knells, knells,
  In a happy Runic rhyme,
  To the rolling of the bells—
  Of the bells, bells, bells:—
  To the tolling of the bells—
Of the bells, bells, bells, bells,
    Bells, bells, bells—
To the moaning and the groaning of the bells.

THE CHAMBERED NAUTILUS

Oliver Wendell Holmes

This is the ship of pearl, which, poets feign,
   Sails the unshadowed main,—
   The venturous bark that flings
On the sweet summer wind its purpled wings
In gulfs enchanted, where the Siren sings,
   And coral reefs lie bare,
Where the cold sea-maids rise to sun their streaming hair.

Its webs of living gauze no more unfurl;
   Wrecked is the ship of pearl!
   And every chambered cell,
Where its dim dreaming life was wont to dwell,
As the frail tenant shaped his growing shell,
   Before thee lies revealed,—
Its irised ceiling rent, its sunless crypt unsealed!

Year after year beheld the silent toil
   That spread his lustrous coil;
   Still, as the spiral grew,
He left the past year's dwelling for the new,
Stole with soft step its shining archway through,
   Built up its idle door,
Stretched in his last-found home, and knew the old no more.

Thanks for the heavenly message brought by thee,
   Child of the wandering sea,
   Cast from her lap, forlorn!
From thy dead lips a clearer note is born
Than ever Triton blew from wreathèd horn!
   While on mine ear it rings,
Through the deep caves of thought I hear a voice that sings:—

Build thee more stately mansions, O my soul,
   As the swift seasons roll!
   Leave thy low-vaulted past!
Let each new temple, nobler than the last,
Shut thee from heaven with a dome more vast,
   Till thou at length art free,
Leaving thine outgrown shell by life's unresting sea!

RECESSIONAL
Rudyard Kipling

God of our fathers, known of old—
Lord of our far-flung battle line—
Beneath Whose awful hand we hold
Dominion over palm and pine—
Lord God of Hosts, be with us yet,
Lest we forget—lest we forget!

The tumult and the shouting dies;
The captains and the kings depart:
Still stands Thine ancient Sacrifice,
An humble and a contrite heart.
Lord God of Hosts, be with us yet,
Lest we forget—lest we forget!

Far-called, our navies melt away;
On dune and headland sinks the fire:
Lo, all our pomp of yesterday
Is one with Nineveh and Tyre!
Judge of the Nations, spare us yet,
Lest we forget—lest we forget!

If, drunk with sight of power, we loose
Wild tongues that have not Thee in awe—
Such boasting as the Gentiles use
Or lesser breeds without the Law—
Lord God of Hosts, be with us yet,
Lest we forget—lest we forget!

For heathen heart that puts her trust
In reeking tube and iron shard—
All valiant dust that builds on dust,
And guarding, calls not Thee to guard—
For frantic boast and foolish word,
Thy mercy on Thy people, Lord!
Amen.

Part X: STORY POEMS

THE HIGHWAYMAN*
Alfred Noyes

PART ONE

The wind was a torrent of darkness among the gusty trees,
The moon was a ghostly galleon tossed upon cloudy seas,
The road was a ribbon of moonlight over the purple moor,
      And the highwayman came riding,
        Riding, riding,
The highwayman came riding, up to the old inn-door.

He'd a French cocked-hat on his forehead, a bunch of lace at his
    chin,
A coat of the claret velvet, and breeches of brown doeskin;
They fitted with never a wrinkle; his boots were up to the thigh!
      And he rode with a jeweled twinkle,
        His pistol butts a-twinkle,
His rapier hilt a-twinkle, under the jeweled sky.

Over the cobbles he clattered and clashed in the dark inn-yard,
And he tapped with his whip on the shutters, but all was locked
    and barred;
He whistled a tune to the window, and who should be waiting there
      But the landlord's black-eyed daughter,
        Bess, the landlord's daughter,
Plaiting a dark red love knot into her long black hair.

*Reprinted by permission of the publishers, J. B. Lippincott Company, from *Collected Poems in One Volume*, by Alfred Noyes. Copyright, 1906, 1922, 1947, by Alfred Noyes.

And dark in the dark old inn-yard a stable-wicket creaked
Where Tim the ostler listened; his face was white and peaked;
His eyes were hollows of madness, his hair like moldy hay,
        But he loved the landlord's daughter,
        The landlord's red-lipped daughter,
Dumb as a dog he listened, and he heard the robber say:

"One kiss, my bonny sweetheart, I'm after a prize tonight,
But I shall be back with the yellow gold before the morning light;
Yet, if they press me sharply, and harry me through the day,
        Then look for me by moonlight,
        Watch for me by moonlight,
I'll come to thee by moonlight, though hell should bar the way."

He rose upright in the stirrups; he scarce could reach her hand,
But she loosened her hair i' the casement! His face burnt like a
    brand
As the black cascade of perfume came tumbling over his breast;
        And he kissed its waves in the moonlight,
        (Oh, sweet black waves in the moonlight!)
Then he tugged at his rein in the moonlight, and galloped away to
    the West.

PART TWO

He did not come in the dawning: he did not come at noon;
And out o' the tawny sunset, before the rise o' the moon,
When the road was a gypsy's ribbon, looping the purple moor,
        A red-coat troop came marching,
        Marching, marching,
King George's men came marching, up to the old inn-door.

They said no word to the landlord, they drank his ale instead,
But they gagged his daughter and bound her to the foot of her nar-
    row bed;
Two of them knelt at her casement, with muskets at their side!
        There was death at every window;
        And hell at one dark window;
For Bess could see, through her casement, the road that *he* would
    ride.

They had tied her up to attention, with many a sniggering jest;
They had bound a musket beside her, with the barrel beneath her
    breast!

291

"Now keep good watch!" and they kissed her.
She heard the dead man say—
   Look for me by moonlight;
   Watch for me by moonlight;
I'll come to thee by moonlight, though hell should bar the way!

She twisted her hands behind her; but all the knots held good!
She writhed her hands till her fingers were wet with sweat or blood!
They stretched and strained in the darkness, and the hours crawled
 by like years,
   Till, now, on the stroke of midnight,
   Cold, on the stroke of midnight,
The tip of one finger touched it! The trigger at least was hers!

The tip of one finger touched it; she strove no more for the rest!
Up, she stood up to attention, with the barrel beneath her breast,
She would not risk their hearing! she would not strive again;
   For the road lay bare in the moonlight,
   Blank and bare in the moonlight;
And the blood of her veins in the moonlight throbbed to her love's
 refrain.

Tlot-tlot, tlot-tlot! Had they heard it? The horse-hoofs ringing clear;
Tlot-tlot, tlot-tlot, in the distance? Were they deaf that they did
 not hear?
Down the ribbon of moonlight, over the brow of the hill,
   The highwayman came riding,
   Riding, riding!
The red-coats looked to their priming! She stood up, straight and
 still!

Tlot-tlot, in the frosty silence! *Tlot-tlot,* in the echoing night!
Nearer he came and nearer! Her face was like a light!
Her eyes grew wide for a moment! she drew one last deep breath,
   Then her finger moved in the moonlight,
   Her musket shattered the moonlight,
Shattered her breast in the moonlight and warned him—with her
 death.

He turned; he spurred to the West; he did not know she stood
Bowed, with her head o'er the musket, drenched with her own red
 blood!
Not till the dawn he heard it; his face grew gray to hear

How Bess, the landlord's daughter,
The landlord's black-eyed daughter,
Had watched for her love in the moonlight, and died in the darkness there.

Back, he spurred like a madman, shrieking a curse to the sky,
With the white road smoking behind him and his rapier brandished high!
Blood-red were his spurs i' the golden noon; wine-red was his velvet coat,
When they shot him down on the highway,
Down like a dog on the highway,
And he lay in his blood on the highway, with the bunch of lace at his throat.

And still of a winter's night, they say, when the wind is in the trees,
When the moon is a ghostly galleon tossed upon cloudy seas,
When the road is a ribbon of moonlight over the purple moor,
A highwayman comes riding,
Riding, riding,
A highwayman comes riding, up to the old inn-door.

Over the cobbles he clatters and clangs in the dark inn-yard;
He taps with his whip on the shutters, but all is locked and barred;
He whistles a tune to the window, and who should be waiting there
But the landlord's black-eyed daughter,
Bess, the landlord's daughter,
Plaiting a dark red love knot into her long black hair.

THE PIED PIPER OF HAMELIN
Robert Browning

Hamelin Town's in Brunswick,
By famous Hanover city;
   The river Weser, deep and wide,
   Washes its wall on the southern side;
   A pleasanter spot you never spied;
But when begins my ditty,
   Almost five hundred years ago,
   To see the townsfolk suffer so
     From vermin, was a pity.

   Rats!
They fought the dogs and killed the cats,
   And bit the babies in the cradles,
And ate the cheeses out of the vats,
   And licked the soup from the cooks' own ladles,
Split open the kegs of salted sprats,
Made nests inside men's Sunday hats,
And even spoiled the women's chats
   By drowning their speaking
   With shrieking and squeaking
In fifty different sharps and flats.

At last the people in a body
   To the Town Hall came flocking:
" 'T is clear," cried they, "our Mayor's a noddy;
   And as for our Corporation—shocking
To think we buy gowns lined with ermine
For dolts that can't or won't determine
What's best to rid us of our vermin!
You hope, because you're old and obese,
To find in the furry civic robe ease?

294

Rouse up, sirs! Give your brains a racking
To find the remedy we're lacking,
Or, sure as fate, we'll send you packing!"
At this the Mayor and Corporation
Quaked with a mighty consternation.

An hour they sat in council;
   At length the Mayor broke silence:
"For a guilder I'd my ermine gown sell,
   I wish I were a mile hence!
It's easy to bid one rack one's brain—
I'm sure my poor head aches again,
I've scratched it so, and all in vain.
Oh for a trap, a trap, a trap!"
Just as he said this, what should hap
At the chamber door but a gentle tap?
"Bless us," cried the Mayor, "what's that?"
(With the Corporation as he sat,
Looking little though wondrous fat;
Nor brighter was his eye, nor moister
Than a too-long-opened oyster,
Save when at noon his paunch grew mutinous
For a plate of turtle green and glutinous.)
"Only a scraping of shoes on the mat?
Anything like the sound of a rat
Makes my heart go pit-a-pat!"

"Come in!" the Mayor cried, looking bigger;
And in did come the strangest figure!
His queer long coat from heel to head
Was half of yellow and half of red,
And he himself was tall and thin,
With sharp blue eyes, each like a pin,
And light loose hair, yet swarthy skin,
No tuft on cheek nor beard on chin,
But lips where smiles went out and in;
There was no guessing his kith and kin:
And nobody could enough admire
The tall man and his quaint attire.
Quoth one: "It's as my great-grandsire,
Starting up at the Trump of Doom's tone,
Had walked this way from his painted tombstone!"

He advanced to the council-table:
And, "Please your honors," said he, "I'm able,
By means of a secret charm, to draw
All creatures living beneath the sun,
That creep or swim or fly or run,
After me so you never saw!
And I chiefly use my charm
On creatures that do people harm,
The mole and toad and newt and viper;
And people call me the Pied Piper."
(And here they noticed round his neck
A scarf of red and yellow stripe,
To match with his coat of the selfsame check;
And at the scarf's end hung a pipe;
And his fingers, they noticed, were ever straying
As if impatient to be playing
Upon this pipe, as low it dangled
Over his vesture so old-fangled.)
"Yet," said he, "poor piper as I am,
In Tartary I freed the Cham,
Last June, from his huge swarms of gnats;
I eased in Asia the Nizam

Of a monstrous brood of vampire-bats:
And as for what your brain bewilders,
If I can rid your town of rats
Will you give me a thousand guilders?"
"One? fifty thousand!"—was the exclamation
Of the astonished Mayor and Corporation.

Into the street the Piper stept,
   Smiling first a little smile,
As if he knew what magic slept
   In his quiet pipe the while;
Then, like a musical adept,
To blow the pipe his lips he wrinkled,
And green and blue his sharp eyes twinkled,
Like a candle-flame where salt is sprinkled;
And ere three shrill notes the pipe uttered,
You heard as if an army muttered;
And the muttering grew to a grumbling;
And the grumbling grew to a mighty rumbling;
And out of the houses the rats came tumbling.
Great rats, small rats, lean rats, brawny rats,
Brown rats, black rats, gray rats, tawny rats,

Grave old plodders, gay young friskers,
  Fathers, mothers, uncles, cousins,
Cocking tails and pricking whiskers,
  Families by tens and dozens,
Brothers, sisters, husbands, wives—
Followed the Piper for their lives.
From street to street he piped advancing,
And step for step they followed dancing,
Until they came to the river Weser,
Wherein all plunged and perished!
—Save one who, stout as Julius Cæsar,
Swam across and lived to carry
(As he, the manuscript he cherished)
To Rat-land home his commentary:
Which was, "At the first shrill notes of the pipe,
I heard a sound as of scraping tripe,
And putting apples, wondrous ripe,
Into a cider-press's gripe:
And a moving away of pickle-tub boards
And a leaving ajar of conserve-cupboards,
And a drawing the corks of train-oil flasks,
And a breaking the hoops of butter casks:
And it seemed as if a voice
(Sweeter far than by harp or by psaltery
Is breathed) called out, 'Oh rats, rejoice!
The world is grown to one vast drysaltery!
So munch on, crunch on, take your nuncheon,
Breakfast, supper, dinner, luncheon!'
And just as a bulky sugar-puncheon,
Already staved, like a great sun shone
Glorious scarce an inch before me,
Just as methought it said, 'Come, bore me!'
—I found the Weser rolling o'er me."

You should have heard the Hamelin people
Ringing the bells till they rocked the steeple.
"Go," cried the Mayor, "and get long poles,
Poke out the nests and block up the holes!
Consult with carpenters and builders,
And leave in our town not even a trace
Of the rats!"—when suddenly, up the face
Of the Piper perked in the market place,
With a "First, if you please, my thousand guilders!"

298

A thousand guilders! The Mayor looked blue;
So did the Corporation too.
For council dinners made rare havoc
With Claret, Moselle, Vin-de-Grave, Hock;
And half the money would replenish
Their cellar's biggest butt with Rhenish.
To pay this sum to a wandering fellow
With a gypsy coat of red and yellow!
"Besides," quoth the Mayor with a knowing wink,
"Our business was done at the river's brink;
We saw with our eyes the vermin sink,
And what's dead can't come to life, I think,
So, friend, we're not the folks to shrink
From the duty of giving you something for drink,
And a matter of money to put in your poke;
But as for the guilders, what we spoke
Of them, as you very well know, was in joke.
Besides, our losses have made us thrifty.
A thousand guilders! Come, take fifty!"

The Piper's face fell, and he cried,
"No trifling! I can't wait, beside!
I've promised to visit by dinnertime
Bagdat, and accept the prime
Of the Head-Cook's pottage, all he's rich in,
For having left, in the Caliph's kitchen,
Of a nest of scorpions no survivor:
With him I proved no bargain-driver,
With you, don't think I'll bate a stiver!
And folks who put me in a passion
May find me pipe after another fashion."

299

"How?" cried the Mayor, "d' ye think I brook
Being worse treated than a Cook?
Insulted by a lazy ribald
With idle pipe and vesture piebald?
You threaten us, fellow? Do your worst,
Blow your pipe there till you burst!"

Once more he stept into the street,
　　And to his lips again
Laid his long pipe of smooth straight cane;
　　And ere he blew three notes (such sweet
Soft notes as yet musician's cunning
　　Never gave the enraptured air)
There was a rustling that seemed like a bustling
Of merry crowds justling at pitching and hustling;
Small feet were pattering, wooden shoes clattering,
Little hands clapping and little tongues chattering,
And, like fowls in a farmyard when barley is scattering,
Out came the children running.
All the little boys and girls,
With rosy cheeks and flaxen curls,
And sparkling eyes and teeth like pearls,
Tripping and skipping, ran merrily after
The wonderful music with shouting and laughter.

The Mayor was dumb, and the Council stood
As if they were changed into blocks of wood,
Unable to move a step, or cry
To the children merrily skipping by,
—Could only follow with the eye
That joyous crowd at the Piper's back.
But how the Mayor was on the rack,
And the wretched Council's bosoms beat,
As the Piper turned from the High Street
To where the Weser rolled its waters
Right in the way of their sons and daughters!
However, he turned from South to West,
And to Koppelberg Hill his steps addressed,
And after him the children pressed;
Great was the joy in every breast.
"He never can cross that mighty top!
He's forced to let the piping drop,
And we shall see our children stop!"

When, lo, as they reached the mountainside,
A wondrous portal opened wide,
As if a cavern was suddenly hollowed;
And the Piper advanced and the children followed,
And when all were in to the very last,
The door in the mountainside shut fast.
Did I say, all? No! One was lame,
And could not dance the whole of the way;
And in after years, if you would blame
His sadness, he was used to say,—
"It's dull in our town since my playmates left!
I can't forget that I'm bereft
Of all the pleasant sights they see,
Which the Piper also promised me.
For he led us, he said, to a joyous land,
Joining the town and just at hand,
Where waters gushed and fruit trees grew
And flowers put forth a fairer hue,
And everything was strange and new;
The sparrows were brighter than peacocks here,
And their dogs outran our fallow deer,
And honeybees had lost their stings,
And horses were born with eagles' wings:
And just as I became assured
My lame foot would be speedily cured,
The music stopped and I stood still,
And found myself outside the hill,
Left alone against my will,
To go now limping as before,
And never hear of that country more!"

Alas, alas! for Hamelin!
   There came into many a burgher's pate
   A text which says that heaven's gate
   Opes to the rich at as easy rate
As the needle's eye takes a camel in!
The Mayor sent East, West, North, and South,
To offer the Piper, by word of mouth,
   Wherever it was men's lot to find him,
Silver and gold to his heart's content,
If he'd only return the way he went,
   And bring the children behind him.
But when they saw 't was a lost endeavor,

302

And Piper and dancers were gone forever,
They made a decree that lawyers never
   Should think their records dated duly
If, after the day of the month and year,
These words did not as well appear,
"And so long after what happened here
   On the Twenty-second of July,
Thirteen hundred and seventy-six:"
And the better in memory to fix
The place of the children's last retreat,

They called it the Pied Piper's Street—
Where any one playing on pipe or tabor
Was sure for the future to lose his labor.
Nor suffered they hostelry or tavern
   To shock with mirth a street so solemn;
But opposite the place of the cavern
   They wrote the story on a column,
And on the great church-window painted
The same, to make the world acquainted
How their children were stolen away,
And there it stands to this very day.
And I must not omit to say

That in Transylvania there's a tribe
Of alien people who ascribe
The outlandish ways and dress
On which their neighbors lay such stress,
To their fathers and mothers having risen
Out of some subterraneous prison
Into which they were trepanned
Long time ago in a mighty band
Out of Hamelin town in Brunswick land,
But how or why, they don't understand.

So, Willy, let me and you be wipers
Of scores out with all men—especially pipers!
And, whether they pipe us free from rats or from mice,
If we've promised them aught, let us keep our promise!

M.W. Tarrant

THE EAGLE

Alfred Tennyson

He clasps the crag with crooked hands;
Close to the sun in lonely lands,
Ringed with the azure world, he stands.

The wrinkled sea beneath him crawls;
He watches from his mountain walls,
And like a thunderbolt he falls.

HIAWATHA'S CHILDHOOD
Henry Wadsworth Longfellow

By the shores of Gitche Gumee,
By the shining Big-Sea-Water,
Stood the wigwam of Nokomis,
Daughter of the Moon, Nokomis.
Dark behind it rose the forest,
Rose the black and gloomy pine trees,
Rose the firs with cones upon them;
Bright before it beat the water,
Beat the clear and sunny water,
Beat the shining Big-Sea-Water.
   There the wrinkled old Nokomis
Nursed the little Hiawatha,
Rocked him in his linden cradle,
Bedded soft in moss and rushes,
Safely bound with reindeer sinews;
Stilled his fretful wail by saying,
"Hush! the Naked Bear will hear thee!"
Lulled him into slumber, singing,
"Ewa-yea! my little owlet!
Who is this that lights the wigwam?
With his great eyes lights the wigwam?
Ewa-yea! my little owlet!"
   Many things Nokomis taught him

Of the stars that shine in heaven;
Showed him Ishkoodah, the comet,
Ishkoodah, with fiery tresses;
Showed the Death-Dance of the spirits,
Warriors with their plumes and war-clubs,
Flaring far away to northward
In the frosty nights of winter;
Showed the broad, white road in heaven,
Pathway of the ghosts, the shadows,
Running straight across the heavens,
Crowded with the ghosts, the shadows.

At the door on summer evenings
Sat the little Hiawatha;
Heard the whispering of the pine trees,
Heard the lapping of the water,
Sounds of music, words of wonder;
"Minne-wawa!" said the pine trees,
"Mudway-aushka!" said the water.

Saw the firefly, Wah-wah-taysee,
Flitting through the dusk of evening,
With the twinkle of its candle
Lighting up the brakes and bushes,
And he sang the song of children,
Sang the song Nokomis taught him:
"Wah-wah-taysee, little firefly
Little, flitting, white-fire insect,
Little, dancing, white-fire creature,
Light me with your little candle,
Ere upon my bed I lay me,
Ere in sleep I close my eyelids!"

Saw the moon rise from the water
Rippling, rounding from the water,
Saw the flecks and shadows on it,
Whispered, "What is that, Nokomis?"
And the good Nokomis answered:
"Once a warrior, very angry,
Seized his grandmother, and threw her
Up into the sky at midnight;
Right against the moon he threw her;
'T is her body that you see there."
Saw the rainbow in the heaven,
In the eastern sky, the rainbow,
Whispered, "What is that, Nokomis?"
And the good Nokomis answered:
" 'T is the heaven of flowers you see there;
All the wild flowers of the forest,
All the lilies of the prairie,
When on earth they fade and perish,
Blossom in that heaven above us."
When he heard the owls at midnight,
Hooting, laughing in the forest,
"What is that?" he cried in terror;
"What is that?" he said, "Nokomis?"
And the good Nokomis answered:
"That is but the owl and owlet,
Talking in their native language,
Talking, scolding at each other."
Then the little Hiawatha
Learned of every bird its language,
Learned their names and all their secrets,
How they built their nests in Summer,
Where they hid themselves in Winter,
Talked with them whene'er he met them,
Called them "Hiawatha's chickens."
Of all beasts he learned the language,
Learned their names and all their secrets,
How the beavers built their lodges,
Where the squirrels hid their acorns,
How the reindeer ran so swiftly,
Why the rabbit was so timid,
Talked with them whene'er he met them,
Called them "Hiawatha's brothers."

SNOWBOUND

John Greenleaf Whittier

The sun that brief December day
Rose cheerless over hills of gray,
And, darkly circled, gave at noon
A sadder light than waning moon.
Slow tracing down the thickening sky
Its mute and ominous prophecy.

. . . .

The wind blew east; we heard the roar
Of Ocean on his wintry shore,
And felt the strong pulse throbbing there
Beat with low rhythm our inland air.

Meanwhile we did our nightly chores,—
Brought in the wood from out-of-doors,
Littered the stalls, and from the mows
Raked down the herd's-grass for the cows:
Heard the horse whinnying for his corn;
And, sharply clashing horn on horn,
Impatient down the stanchion rows
The cattle shake their walnut bows;
While, peering from his early perch
Upon the scaffold's pole of birch
The cock his crested helmet bent
And down his querulous challenge sent.

Unwarned by any sunset light
The gray day darkened into night,
A night made hoary with the swarm
And whirl-dance of the blinding storm,
As zigzag, wavering to and fro
Crossed and recrossed the winged snow:
And ere the early bedtime came
The white drift piled the window-frame,
And through the glass the clothesline posts
Looked in like tall and sheeted ghosts.

So all night long the storm roared on:
The morning broke without a sun;
In tiny spherule traced with lines
Of Nature's geometric signs,

308

In starry flake, and pellicle
All day the hoary meteor fell;
And, when the second morning shone,
We looked upon a world unknown,
On nothing we could call our own.
Around the glistening wonder bent
The blue walls of the firmament,
No cloud above, no earth below,—
A universe of sky and snow!
The old familiar sights of ours
Took marvelous shapes; strange domes and towers
Rose up where sty or corn-crib stood,
Or garden-wall, or belt of wood;
A smooth white mound the brush-pile showed,
A fenceless drift what once was road.
The bridle-post an old man sat
With loose-flung coat and high cocked hat;
The well-curb had a Chinese roof;
And even the long sweep, high aloof,
In its slant splendor, seemed to tell
Of Pisa's leaning miracle.

.   .   .   .

Shut in from all the world without,
We sat the clean-winged hearth about,
Content to let the north-wind roar
In baffled rage at pane and door,
While the red logs before us beat
The frost-line back with tropic heat;
And ever, when a louder blast
Shook beam and rafter as it passed,
The merrier up its roaring draught
The great throat of the chimney laughed,
The house-dog on his paws outspread
Laid to the fire his drowsy head,
The cat's dark silhouette on the wall
A couchant tiger's seemed to fall;
And, for the winter fireside meet,
Between the andirons' straddling feet,
The mug of cider simmered slow,
The apples sputtered in a row,
And, close at hand, the basket stood
With nuts from brown October's wood.

LITTLE ORPHANT ANNIE

James Whitcomb Riley

Little Orphant Annie's come to our house to stay,
An' wash the cups and saucers up, and brush the crumbs away,
An' shoo the chickens off the porch, an' dust the hearth, an' sweep,
An' make the fire, an' bake the bread, an' earn her board-an'-keep;
An' all us other children, when the supper things is done,
We set around the kitchen fire an' has the mostest fun
A-list'nin' to the witch-tales 'at Annie tells about,
An' the Gobble-uns 'at gits you
                    Ef you
                        Don't
                            Watch
                            Out!

Onc't they was a little boy wouldn't say his pray'rs—
An' when he went to bed at night, away up stairs,
His mammy heerd him holler, an' his daddy heerd him bawl,
An' when they turn't the kivvers down, he wasn't there at all!
An' they seeked him in the rafter-room, an' cubby-hole, an' press.
An' seeked him up the chimbly-flue, an' ever'wheres, I guess;
But all they ever found was thist his pants an' roundabout!
An' the Gobble-uns 'll git you
                    Ef you
                        Don't
                            Watch
                            Out!

An' one time a little girl 'ud allus laugh an' grin,
An' make fun of ever' one, an' all her blood-an'-kin;
An' onc't when they was "company," an' ole folks was there.
She mocked 'em an' shocked 'em, an' said she didn't care!
An' thist as she kicked her heels, an' turn't to run an' hide,
They was two great big Black Things a-standin' by her side,
An' they snatched her through the ceilin' 'fore she knowed what
    she's about!
An' the Gobble-uns 'll git you
               Ef you
            Don't
               Watch
               Out!

An' little Orphant Annie says, when the blaze is blue,
An' the lampwick sputters, an' the wind goes woo-oo!
An' you hear the crickets quit, an' the moon is gray,
An' the lightnin' bugs in dew is all squenched away,—
You better mind yer parents, and yer teachers fond and dear,
An' churish them 'at loves you, an' dry the orphant's tear,
An' help the pore an' needy ones 'at clusters all about,
Er the Gobble-uns 'll git you
               Ef you
            Don't
               Watch
               Out!

THE RAGGEDY MAN

James Whitcomb Riley

O The Raggedy Man! He works for Pa;
An' he's the goodest man ever you saw!
He comes to our house every day,
An' waters the horses, an' feeds 'em hay;
An' he opens the shed—an' we all ist laugh
When he drives out our little old wobblely calf;
An' nen—ef our hired girl says he can—
He milks the cow for 'Lizabuth Ann.—
    Ain't he a' awful good Raggedy Man?
    Raggedy! Raggedy! Raggedy Man!

W'y, The Raggedy Man—he's ist so good
He splits the kindlin' an' chops the wood;
An' nen he spades in our garden, too,
An' does most things 'at boys can't do!—
He clumbed clean up in our big tree
An' shooked a' apple down fer me—
An' nother'n, too, fer 'Lizabuth Ann—
An' nother'n, too, fer The Raggedy Man—
    Ain't he a' awful kind Raggedy Man?
        Raggedy! Raggedy! Raggedy Man!

An' The Raggedy Man, he knows most rhymes
An' tells 'em, ef I be good, sometimes:
Knows 'bout Giunts, an' Griffuns, an' Elves,
'An' the Squidgicum-Squees 'at swallers therselves!
An', wite by the pump in our pasture-lot,
He showed me the hole 'at the Wunks is got,
'At lives 'way deep in the ground, an' can
Turn into me, er 'Lizabuth Ann!
    Ain't he a funny old Raggedy Man?
        Raggedy! Raggedy! Raggedy Man!

The Raggedy Man—one time when he
Wuz makin' a little bow-'n'-orry fer me,
Says, "When you're big like your Pa is,
Air you go' to keep a fine store like his—
An' be a rich merchunt—an' wear fine clothes?—
Er what air you go' to be, goodness knows!"
An' nen he laughed at 'Lizabuth Ann,
An' I says, "'M go' to be a Raggedy Man!
    I'm ist go' to be a nice Raggedy Man!
        Raggedy! Raggedy! Raggedy Man!"

JEST 'FORE CHRISTMAS
Eugene Field

Father calls me William, sister calls me Will,
Mother calls me Willie, but the fellers call me Bill!
Mighty glad I ain't a girl—ruther be a boy,
Without them sashes, curls, an' things that's worn by Fauntleroy!

Love to chawnk green apples an' go swimmin' in the lake—
Hate to take the castor-ile they give for belly-ache!
'Most all the time, the whole year round, there ain't no flies on me,
But jest 'fore Christmas I'm as good as I kin be!

Got a yeller dog named Sport, sick him on the cat;
First thing she knows she doesn't know where she is at!
Got a clipper sled, an' when us kids goes out to slide,
'Long comes the grocery cart, an' we all hook a ride!
But sometimes when the grocery man is worrited an' cross,
He reaches at us with his whip, an' larrups up his hoss,
An' then I laff and holler, "Oh, ye never teched *me!*"
But jest 'fore Christmas I'm as good as I kin be!

Gran'ma says she hopes that when I git to be a man,
I'll be a missionarer like her oldest brother, Dan . . .
But gran'ma she has never been to see a Wild West show,
Nor read the Life of Daniel Boone, or else I guess she'd know
That Buff'lo Bill an' cowboys is good enough for me!
Excep' jest 'fore Christmas when I'm as good as I kin be!

And then old Sport he hangs around, so solemn-like an' still
His eyes they keep a-sayin': "What's the matter, little Bill?"
The old cat sneaks down off her perch an' wonders what's become
Of them two enemies of hern that used to make things hum!
But I am so perlite an' tend so earnestly to biz,
That mother says to father: "How improved our Willie is!"
But father, havin' been a boy hisself, suspicions me
When, jest 'fore Christmas I'm as good as I kin be!

For Christmas, with its lots an' lots of candies, cakes, an' toys,
Was made, they say, for proper kids an' not for naughty boys;
So wash yer face an' bresh yer hair, an' mind yer p's an' q's,
An' don't bust out yer pantaloons, an' don't wear out yer shoes;
Say "Yessum" to the ladies, and "Yessur" to the men,
An' when they's company, don't pass yer plate for pie again;
But, thinkin' of the things yer'd like to see upon that tree,
Jest 'fore Christmas be as good as yer kin be!

THE VILLAGE BLACKSMITH
Henry Wadsworth Longfellow

Under a spreading chestnut tree
   The village smithy stands;
The smith, a mighty man is he,
   With large and sinewy hands;
And the muscles of his brawny arms
   Are strong as iron bands.

His hair is crisp, and black, and long,
   His face is like the tan;
His brow is wet with honest sweat,
   He earns whate'er he can,
And looks the whole world in the face,
   For he owes not any man.

Week in, week out, from morn till night,
   You can hear his bellows blow;
You can hear him swing his heavy sledge,
   With measured beat and slow
Like a sexton ringing the village bell,
   When the evening sun is low.

And children coming home from school
   Look in at the open door;
They love to see the flaming forge,
   And hear the bellows roar,
And catch the burning sparks that fly
   Like chaff from a threshing-floor.

He goes on Sunday to the church,
   And sits among his boys;
He hears the parson pray and preach,
   He hears his daughter's voice,
Singing in the village choir,
   And it makes his heart rejoice.

It sounds to him like her mother's voice,
    Singing in Paradise!
He needs must think of her once more,
    How in the grave she lies;
And with his hard, rough hand he wipes
    A tear out of his eyes.

Toiling,—rejoicing,—sorrowing,
    Onward through life he goes;
Each morning sees some task begin,
    Each evening sees it close;
Something attempted, something done,
    Has earned a night's repose.

Thanks, thanks to thee, my worthy friend,
    For the lesson thou hast taught!
Thus at the flaming forge of life
    Our fortunes must be wrought;
Thus on its sounding anvil shaped
    Each burning deed and thought.

LOCHINVAR

Sir Walter Scott

Oh, young Lochinvar is come out of the west,
Through all the wide Border his steed was the best;
And save his good broadsword, he weapon had none,
He rode all unarmed, and he rode all alone.
So faithful in love, and so dauntless in war,
There never was knight like the young Lochinvar.

He stayed not for brake, and he stopped not for stone,
He swam the Eske river where ford there was none;
But ere he alighted at Netherby gate,
The bride had consented, the gallant came late;
For a laggard in love, and a dastard in war,
Was to wed the fair Ellen of brave Lochinvar.

So boldly he entered the Netherby Hall,
Among bridesmen, and kinsmen, and brothers, and all:
Then spoke the bride's father, his hand on his sword
(For the poor craven bridegroom said never a word),
"Oh, come ye in peace here, or come ye in war,
Or to dance at our bridal, young Lord Lochinvar?"

"I long wooed your daughter, my suit you denied;—
Love swells like the Solway, but ebbs like its tide—
And now am I come, with this lost love of mine,
To lead but one measure, drink one cup of wine.
There are maidens in Scotland more lovely by far,
That would gladly be bride to the young Lochinvar."

The bride kissed the goblet: the knight took it up,
He quaffed off the wine, and he threw down the cup.
She looked down to blush, and she looked up to sigh,
With a smile on her lips, and a tear in her eye.
He took her soft hand, ere her mother could bar,—
"Now tread we a measure!" said young Lochinvar.

So stately his form, and so lovely her face,
That never a hall such a galliard did grace;
While her mother did fret, and her father did fume,
And the bridegroom stood dangling his bonnet and plume;
And the bride-maidens whispered, " 'T were better by far,
To have matched our fair cousin with young Lochinvar."

One touch to her hand, and one word to her ear,
When they reached the hall-door, and the charger stood near;
So light to the croupe the fair lady he swung,
So light to the saddle before her he sprung!
"She is won! we are gone, over bank, bush, and scaur;
They'll have fleet steeds that follow," quoth young Lochinvar.

There was mounting 'mong Graemes of the Netherby clan;
Forsters, Fenwicks, and Musgraves, they rode and they ran:
There was racing and chasing on Cannobie Lee,
But the lost bride of Netherby ne'er did they see.
So daring in love, and so dauntless in war,
Have ye e'er heard of gallant like young Lochinvar?

BUGLE SONG

Alfred Tennyson

The splendor falls on castle walls
  And snowy summits old in story;
The long light shakes across the lakes,
  And the wild cataract leaps in glory.
Blow, bugle, blow, set the wild echoes flying,
Blow, bugle; answer, echoes, dying, dying, dying.

O, hark, O, hear! how thin and clear,
  And thinner, clearer, farther going!
O, sweet and far from cliff and scar
  The horns of Elfland faintly blowing!
Blow, let us hear the purple glens replying;
Blow, bugle; answer, echoes, dying, dying, dying.

O love, they die in yon rich sky,
  They faint on hill or field or river;
Our echoes roll from soul to soul,
  And grow for ever and for ever.
Blow, bugle, blow, set the wild echoes flying,
And answer, echoes, answer, dying, dying, dying.

THE VAGABOND

Robert Louis Stevenson

Give to me the life I love,
  Let the lave go by me,
Give the jolly heaven above
  And the byway nigh me.
Bed in the bush with stars to see,
  Bread I dip in the river—
There's the life for a man like me,
  There's the life forever. . . .

Let the blow fall soon or late,
  Let what will be o'er me;
Give the face of earth around
  And the road before me.
Wealth I seek not, hope nor love,
  Nor a friend to know me;
All I seek the heaven above
  And the road below me.

BOOT AND SADDLE

Robert Browning

Boot, saddle, to horse, and away!
Rescue my castle before the hot day
Brightens to blue from its silvery gray.
 Boot, saddle, to horse, and away!

Ride past the suburbs, asleep as you'd say;
Many's the friend there, will listen and pray,
"God's luck to gallants that strike up the lay—
 Boot, saddle, to horse, and away!"

Forty miles off, like a roebuck at bay,
Flouts Castle Brancepeth the Roundheads' array:
Who laughs, "Good fellows ere this, by my fay,
 Boot, saddle, to horse, and away!"

Who? My wife Gertrude; that, honest and gay,
Laughs when you talk of surrendering, "Nay!
I've better counselors; what counsel they?
 Boot, saddle, to horse, and away!"

HOW THEY BROUGHT THE GOOD NEWS
FROM GHENT TO AIX
Robert Browning

I sprang to the stirrup, and Joris and he;
I galloped, Dirck galloped, we galloped all three;
"Good speed!" cried the watch as the gate-bolts undrew,
"Speed!" echoed the wall to us galloping through.
Behind shut the postern, the lights sank to rest,
And into the midnight we galloped abreast.

Not a word to each other; we kept the great pace
Neck by neck, stride by stride, never changing our place;
I turned in my saddle and made its girths tight,
Then shortened each stirrup and set the pique right,
Rebuckled the cheek-strap, chained slacker the bit,
Nor galloped less steadily Roland a whit.

'Twas a moonset at starting; but while we drew near
Lokeren, the cocks crew and twilight dawned clear;
At Boom a great yellow star came out to see;
At Düffeld 'twas morning as plain as could be;
And from Mecheln church-steeple we heard the half-chime,—
So Joris broke silence with "Yet there is time!"

At Aerschot up leaped of a sudden the sun,
And against him the cattle stood black every one,
To stare through the mist at us galloping past;
And I saw my stout galloper Roland at last,
With resolute shoulders, each butting away
The haze, as some bluff river headland its spray;

And his low head and crest, just one sharp ear bent back
For my voice, and the other pricked out on his track;
And one eye's black intelligence,—ever that glance
O'er its white edge at me, his own master, askance;
And the thick heavy spume-flakes, which aye and anon
His fierce lips shook upward in galloping on.

By Hasselt Dirck groaned; and cried Joris, "Stay spur!
Your Roos galloped bravely, the fault's not in her;
We'll remember at Aix,"—for one heard the quick wheeze
Of her chest, saw the stretched neck, and staggering knees,
And sunk tail, and horrible heave of the flank,
As down on her haunches she shuddered and sank.

So we were left galloping, Joris and I,
Past Looz and past Tongres, no cloud in the sky;
The broad sun above laughed a pitiless laugh;
'Neath our feet broke the brittle, bright stubble-like chaff;
Till over by Dalhem a dome-spire sprang white,
And "Gallop," gasped Joris, "for Aix is in sight!"

"How they'll greet us!"—and all in a moment his roan
Rolled neck and croup over, lay dead as a stone;
And there was my Roland to bear the whole weight
Of the news which alone could save Aix from her fate,
With his nostrils like pits full of blood to the brim,
And with circles of red for his eye-sockets' rim.

Then I cast loose my buff-coat, each holster let fall,
Shook off both my jack-boots, let go belt and all,
Stood up in the stirrup, leaned, patted his ear,
Called my Roland his pet name, my horse without peer,—
Clapped my hands, laughed and sung, any noise, bad or good,
Till at length into Aix Roland galloped and stood.

And all I remember is friends flocking round,
As I sat with his head 'twixt my knees on the ground;
And no voice but was praising this Roland of mine,
As I poured down his throat our last measure of wine,
Which (the burgesses voted by common consent)
Was no more than his due who brought good news from Ghent.

LADY CLARE

Alfred Tennyson

It was the time when lilies blow,
   And clouds are highest up in air,
Lord Ronald brought a lily-white doe
   To give his cousin, Lady Clare.

I trow they did not part in scorn;
   Lovers long-betrothed were they,
They two will wed the morrow morn;
   God's blessing on the day!

"He does not love me for my birth,
   Nor for my lands so broad and fair;
He loves me for my own true worth,
   And that is well," said Lady Clare.

In there came old Alice the nurse,
   Said, "Who was this that went from thee?"
"It was my cousin," said Lady Clare,
   "Tomorrow he weds with me."

"O God be thanked!" said Alice the nurse,
   "That all comes round so just and fair;
Lord Ronald is heir of all your lands,
   And you are not the Lady Clare."

"Are ye out of your mind, my nurse, my nurse,"
   Said Lady Clare, "that ye speak so wild?"
"As God's above," said Alice the nurse,
   "I speak the truth: you are my child.

"The old Earl's daughter died at my breast;
   I speak the truth, as I live by bread!
I buried her like my own sweet child,
   And put my child in her stead."

"Falsely, falsely have ye done,
   O mother," she said, "if this be true,
To keep the best man under the sun
   So many years from his due."

322

"Nay now, my child," said Alice the nurse,
  "But keep the secret for your life,
And all you have will be Lord Ronald's
  When you are man and wife."

"If I'm a beggar born," she said,
  "I will speak out, for I dare not lie.
Pull off, pull off, the broach of gold,
  And fling the diamond necklace by!"

"Nay now, my child," said Alice the nurse,
  "But keep the secret all ye can."
She said, "Not so: but I will know
  If there be any faith in man."

"Nay now, what faith?" said Alice the nurse,
  "The man will cleave unto his right."
"And he shall have it," the lady replied,
  "Though I should die tonight."

"Yet give one kiss to your mother dear!
  Alas, my child, I sinned for thee."
"O mother, mother, mother," she said,
  "So strange it seems to me!

"Yet here's a kiss for my mother dear,
  My mother dear, if this be so,
And lay your hand upon my head,
  And bless me, mother, ere I go."

She clad herself in a russet gown,
  She was no longer Lady Clare;
She went by dale, and she went by down,
  With a single rose in her hair.

The lily-white doe Lord Ronald had brought
  Leapt up from where she lay,
Dropt her head in the maiden's hand,
  And followed her all the way.

Down stept Lord Ronald from his tower;
   "O Lady Clare, you shame your worth!
Why come you drest like a village maid,
   That are the flower of the earth?"

"If I come drest like a village maid,
   I am but as my fortunes are:
I am a beggar born," she said,
   "And not the Lady Clare."

"Play me no tricks," said Lord Ronald,
   "For I am yours in word and in deed;
"Play me no tricks," said Lord Ronald,
   "Your riddle is hard to read."

Oh, and proudly stood she up!
   Her heart within her did not fail:
She looked into Lord Ronald's eyes,
   And told him all her nurse's tale.

He laughed a laugh of merry scorn;
   He turned, and kissed her where she stood;
"If you are not the heiress born,
   And I," said he, "the next in blood,—

"If you are not the heiress born,
   And I," said he, "the lawful heir,
We two will wed tomorrow morn,
   And you shall still be Lady Clare."

ROBIN HOOD AND ALLEN-A-DALE
Author Unknown

Come listen to me, you gallants so free,
　All you that love mirth for to hear,
And I will tell you of a bold outlaw
　That lived in Nottinghamshire.

As Robin Hood in the forest stood,
　All under the greenwood tree,
There he was aware of a brave young man,
　As fine as fine might be.

The youngster was clothed in scarlet red,
　In scarlet fine and gay;
And he did frisk it over the plain,
　And chanted a roundelay.

As Robin Hood next morning stood
　Amongst the leaves so gay,
There did he espy the same young man,
　Come drooping along the way.

The scarlet he wore the day before
　It was clean cast away;
And at every step he fetched a sigh,
　"Alack and a well-a-day!"

Then stepped forth brave Little John,
　And Midge, the miller's son,
Which made the young man bend his bow,
　When as he saw them come.

"Stand off, stand off!" the young man said,
　"What is your will with me?"
"You must come before our master straight,
　Under yon greenwood tree."

And when he came bold Robin before,
　Robin asked him courteously,
"Oh, hast thou any money to spare
　For my merry men and me?"

"I have no money," the young man said,
　"But five shillings and a ring;
And that I have kept this seven long years,
　To have it at my wedding.

"Yesterday I should have married a maid,
　But she soon from me was tane,
And chosen to be an old knight's delight,
　Whereby my poor heart is slain."

"What is thy name?" then said Robin Hood,
　"Come tell me without any fail":
"By the faith of my body," then said the young man,
　"My name it is Allen-a-Dale."

"What wilt thou give me?" said Robin Hood,
　"In ready gold or fee,
To help thee to thy true love again,
　And deliver her unto thee?"

"I have no money," then quoth the young man,
　"No ready gold nor fee,
But I will swear upon a book
　Thy true servant for to be."

"How many miles is it to thy true love?
　Come tell me without guile."
"By the faith of my body," then said the young man,
　"It is but five little mile."

Then Robin he hasted over the plain,
　He did neither stint nor lin,
Until he came unto the church,
　Where Allen should keep his wedding.

"What hast thou here?" the bishop then said,
  "I prithee now tell unto me":
"I am a bold harper," quoth Robin Hood,
  "And the best in the north country."

"Oh welcome, oh welcome," the bishop he said,
  "That music best pleaseth me";
"You shall have no music," quoth Robin Hood,
  "Till the bride and the bridegroom I see."

With that came in a wealthy knight,
  Which was both grave and old,
And after him a finikin lass,
  Did shine like the glistering gold.

"This is not a fit match," quoth bold Robin Hood,
  "That you do seem to make here,
For since we are come into the church,
  The bride shall choose her own dear."

Then Robin Hood put his horn to his mouth,
  And blew blasts two or three;
When four-and-twenty bowmen bold
  Came leaping over the lea.

And when they came into the churchyard,
  Marching all on a row,
The very first man was Allen-a-Dale,
  To give bold Robin his bow.

"This is thy true love," Robin he said,
  "Young Allen as I hear say;
And you shall be married at this same time,
  Before we depart away."

"That shall not be," the bishop he said,
  "For thy word shall not stand;
They shall be three times asked in the church,
  As the law is of our land."

Robin Hood pulled off the bishop's coat,
    And put it upon Little John;
"By the faith of my body," then Robin said,
    "This cloth doth make thee a man."

When Little John went into the quire;
    The people began to laugh;
He asked them seven times in the church,
    Lest three times should not be enough.

"Who gives me this maid?" said Little John;
    Quoth Robin Hood, "That do I,
And he that takes her from Allen-a-Dale,
    Full dearly he shall her buy."

And thus having end of this merry wedding,
    The bride looked like a queen;
And so they returned to the merry greenwood,
    Amongst the leaves so green.

ABOU BEN ADHEM
Leigh Hunt

Abou Ben Adhem (may his tribe increase!)
Awoke one night from a deep dream of peace,
And saw within the moonlight in the room,
Making it rich and like a lily in bloom,
An angel writing in a book of gold;
Exceeding peace had made Ben Adhem bold,
And to the Presence in the room he said,
"What writest thou?" The vision raised its head,
And with a look made of all sweet accord,
Answered, "The names of those who love the Lord."
"And is mine one?" said Abou. "Nay, not so,"
Replied the angel. Abou spoke more low,
But cheerly still, and said, "I pray thee, then,
Write me as one who loves his fellow men."
The angel wrote and vanished; the next night
He came again with a great wakening light,
And showed the names whom love of God had blest,
And lo! Ben Adhem's name led all the rest.

328

THE CREMATION OF SAM McGEE

Robert W. Service

There are strange things done in the midnight sun
By the men who moil for gold;
The Arctic trails have their secret tales
That would make your blood run cold;
The Northern Lights have seen queer sights,
But the queerest they ever did see
Was that night on the marge of Lake Lebarge
I cremated Sam McGee.

Now Sam McGee was from Tennessee, where the cotton blooms
and blows.
Why he left his home in the South to roam 'round the Pole, God
only knows.
He was always cold, but the land of gold seemed to hold him like
a spell;
Though he'd often say in his homely way that "he'd sooner live in
hell."

On a Christmas day we were mushing our way over the Dawson trail.
Talk of your cold! through the parka's fold it stabbed like a driven
nail.
If our eyes we'd close, then the lashes froze till sometimes we
couldn't see;
It wasn't much fun, but the only one to whimper was Sam McGee.

And that very night, as we lay packed tight in our robes beneath
the snow,
And the dogs were fed, and the stars o'erhead were dancing heel
and toe,
He turned to me, and "Cap," says he, "I'll cash in this trip, I guess;
And if I do, I'm asking that you won't refuse my last request."

Well, he seemed so low that I couldn't say no; then he says with a
sort of moan:
"It's the cursed cold, and it's got right hold till I'm chilled clean
through to the bone.
Yet 'tain't being dead—it's my awful dread of the icy grave that pains;
So I want you to swear that, foul or fair, you'll cremate my last
remains."

A pal's last need is a thing to heed, so I swore I would not fail;
And we started on at the streak of dawn; but God! he looked
  ghastly pale.
He crouched on the sleigh, and he raved all day of his home in
  Tennessee;
And before nightfall a corpse was all that was left of Sam McGee.

There wasn't a breath in that land of death, and I hurried, horror-
  driven,
With a corpse half-hid that I couldn't get rid, because of a promise
  given;
It was lashed to the sleigh, and it seemed to say: "You may tax
  your brawn and brains,
But you promised true, and it's up to you to cremate these last
  remains."

Now a promise made is a debt unpaid, and the trail has its own
  stern code.
In the days to come, though my lips were dumb, in my heart how
  I cursed that load.
In the long, long night, by the lone firelight, while the huskies,
  round in a ring,
Howled out their woes to the homeless snows—O God! how I
  loathed the thing.

And every day that quiet clay seemed to heavy and heavier grow;
And on I went, though the dogs were spent and the grub was get-
  ting low;
The trail was bad, and I felt half mad, but I swore I would not
  give in;
And I'd often sing to the hateful thing, and it harkened with a grin.

Till I came to the marge of Lake Lebarge, and a derelict there lay;
It was jammed in the ice, but I saw in a trice it was called the
  "Alice May."
And I looked at it, and I thought a bit, and I looked at my frozen
  chum;
Then "Here," said I, with a sudden cry, "is my cre-ma-to-re-um."

Some planks I tore from the cabin floor, and I lit the boiler fire;
Some coal I found that was lying around, and I heaped the fuel
  higher;
The flames just soared, and the furnace roared—such a blaze you
  seldom see;
And I burrowed a hole in the glowing coal, and I stuffed in Sam
  McGee.

Then I made a hike, for I didn't like to hear him sizzle so;
And the heavens scowled, and the huskies howled, and the wind
  began to blow.
It was icy cold, but the hot sweat rolled down my cheeks, and I
  don't know why;
And the greasy smoke in an inky cloak went streaking down the sky.

I do not know how long in the snow I wrestled with grisly fear;
But the stars came out and they danced about ere again I ventured
  near;
I was sick with dread, but I bravely said: "I'll just take a peep
  inside.
I guess he's cooked, and it's time I looked"; . . . then the door I
  opened wide.

And there sat Sam, looking cool and calm, in the heart of the
  furnace roar;
And he wore a smile you could see a mile, and he said: "Please
  close that door.
It's fine in here, but I greatly fear you'll let in the cold and storm—
Since I left Plumtree down in Tennessee, it's the first time I've
  been warm."

There are strange things done in the midnight sun
By the men who moil for gold;
The Arctic trails have their secret tales
That would make your blood run cold;
The Northern Lights have seen queer sights,
But the queerest they ever did see
Was that night on the marge of Lake Lebarge
I cremated Sam McGee.

CASEY AT THE BAT

Ernest Lawrence Thayer

It looked extremely rocky for the Mudville nine that day;
The score stood two to four, with but one inning left to play.
So, when Cooney died at second, and Burrows did the same,
A pallor wreathed the features of the patrons of the game.

A straggling few got up to go, leaving there the rest,
With that hope which springs eternal within the human breast.
For they thought: "If only Casey could get a whack at that,"
They'd put even money now, with Casey at the bat.

But Flynn preceded Casey, and likewise so did Blake,
And the former was a pudd'n, and the latter was a fake.
So on that stricken multitude a deathlike silence sat;
For there seemed but little chance of Casey's getting to the bat.

But Flynn let drive a "single," to the wonderment of all.
And the much-despisèd Blakey "tore the cover off the ball."
And when the dust had lifted, and they saw what had occurred,
There was Blakey safe at second, and Flynn a-huggin' third.

Then from the gladdened multitude went up a joyous yell—
It rumbled in the mountaintops, it rattled in the dell;

It struck upon the hillside and rebounded on the flat;
For Casey, mighty Casey, was advancing to the bat.

There was ease in Casey's manner as he stepped into his place,
There was pride in Casey's bearing and a smile on Casey's face;
And when responding to the cheers he lightly doffed his hat,
No stranger in the crowd could doubt 'twas Casey at the bat.

Ten thousand eyes were on him as he rubbed his hands with dirt,
Five thousand tongues applauded when he wiped them on his shirt;
Then when the writhing pitcher ground the ball into his hip,
Defiance glanced in Casey's eye, a sneer curled Casey's lip.

And now the leather-covered sphere came hurtling through the air,
And Casey stood a-watching it in haughty grandeur there.
Close by the sturdy batsman the ball unheeded sped;
"That ain't my style," said Casey. "Strike one," the umpire said.

From the benches, black with people, there went up a muffled roar,
Like the beating of the storm waves on the stern and distant shore.
"Kill him! kill the umpire!" shouted someone on the stand;
And it's likely they'd have killed him had not Casey raised his hand.

With a smile of Christian charity great Casey's visage shone;
He stilled the rising tumult, he made the game go on;
He signaled to the pitcher, and once more the spheroid flew;
But Casey still ignored it, and the umpire said, "Strike two."

"Fraud!" cried the maddened thousands, and the echo answered
    "Fraud!"
But one scornful look from Casey and the audience was awed;
They saw his face grow stern and cold, they saw his muscles strain,
And they knew that Casey wouldn't let the ball go by again.

The sneer is gone from Casey's lips, his teeth are clenched in hate,
He pounds with cruel vengeance his bat upon the plate;
And now the pitcher holds the ball, and now he lets it go,
And now the air is shattered by the force of Casey's blow.

Oh, somewhere in this favored land the sun is shining bright,
The band is playing somewhere, and somewhere hearts are light;
And somewhere men are laughing, and somewhere children shout,
But there is no joy in Mudville—Mighty Casey has struck out.

FORTY SINGING SEAMEN*

Alfred Noyes

Across the seas of Wonderland to Mogadore we plodded,
Forty singing seamen in an old black barque,
And we landed in the twilight where a Polyphemus nodded,
With his battered moon-eye winking red and yellow through the
    dark!
  For his eye was growing mellow,
  Rich and ripe and red and yellow,
As was time, since old Ulysses made him bellow in the dark!
Since Ulysses bunged his eye up with a pine-torch in the dark!

Were they mountains in the gloaming or the giant's ugly shoulders
Just beneath the rolling eye-ball, with its bleared and vinous glow,
Red and yellow o'er the purple of the pines among the boulders
And the shaggy horror brooding on the sullen slopes below,
  Were they pines among the boulders
  Or the hair upon his shoulders?
We were only simple seamen, so of course we didn't know.
We were simple singing seamen, so of course we couldn't know.

But we crossed a plain of poppies, and we came upon a fountain
Not of water, but of jewels, like a spray of leaping fire;
And behind it, in an emerald glade, beneath a golden mountain
There stood a crystal palace, for a sailor to admire;
  For a troop of ghosts came round us,
  Which with leaves of bay they crowned us,
Then with grog they well-nigh drowned us, to the depth of our
    desire!
And 'twas very friendly of them, as a sailor can admire!

There was music all about us, we were growing quite forgetful
We were only singing seamen from the dirt of London-town,
Though the nectar that we swallowed seemed to vanish half regretful
As if we wasn't good enough to take such vittles down,
   When we saw a sudden figger,
   Tall and black as any figger,
Like the devil—only bigger—drawing near us with a frown!
Like the devil—but much bigger—and he wore a golden crown!

And "What's all this?" he growls at us! With dignity we chaunted,
"Forty singing seamen, sir, as won't be put upon!"
"What? Englishmen?" he cries, "Well, if ye don't mind being
    haunted,
Faith, you're welcome to my palace; I'm the famous Prester John!
   Will ye walk into my palace?
   I don't bear 'ee any malice!
One and all ye shall be welcome in the halls of Prester John!"
So we walked into the palace and the halls of Prester John!

Now the door was one great diamond and the hall a hollow ruby—
Big as Beachy Head, my lads, nay, bigger by a half!
And I sees the mate wi' mouth agape, a-staring like a booby,
And the skipper close behind him, with his tongue out like a calf!
   Now the way to take it rightly
   Was to walk along politely
Just as if you didn't notice—so I couldn't help but laugh!
For they both forgot their manners and the crew was bound to
    laugh!

But he took us through his palace, and, my lads, as I'm a sinner,
We walked into an opal like a sunset-colored cloud—
"My dining room," he says, and, quick as light, we saw a dinner
Spread before us by the fingers of a hidden fairy crowd;
   And the skipper, swaying gently
   After dinner, murmurs faintly,
"I looks to-wards you, Prester John, you've done us very proud!"
And he drank his health with honors, for he *done* us *very* proud!

Then he walks us to his gardens where we sees a feathered demon
Very splendid and important on a sort of spicy tree!
"That's the Phoenix," whispers Prester, "which all eddicated seamen
Knows the only one existent, and *he's* waiting for to flee!
   When his hundred years expire

Then he'll set hisself afire
And another from his ashes rise most beautiful to see!
With wings of rose and emerald most beautiful to see!

Then he says, "In yonder forest there's a little silver river
And whosoever drinks of it, his youth will never die!
The centuries go by, but Prester John endures forever
With his music in the mountains and his magic on the sky!
    While *your* hearts are growing colder,
    While your world is growing older,
There's a magic in the distance, where the sea-line meets the sky.
It shall call to singing seamen till the fount o' song is dry!"

So we thought we'd up and seek it, but that forest fair defied us,—
First a crimson leopard laughed at us most horrible to see,
Then a sea-green lion came and sniffed and licked his chops and
    eyed us,
While a red and yellow unicorn was dancing round a tree!
    We was trying to look thinner,
    Which was hard, because our dinner
Must ha' made us very tempting to a cat o' high degree!
Must ha' made us very tempting to the whole menarjeree!

So we scuttled from that forest and across the poppy meadows
Where the awful shaggy horror brooded o'er us in the dark!
And we pushes out from shore again a-jumping at our shadows
And pulls away most joyful to the old black barque!
    And home again we plodded
    While Polyphemus nodded
With his battered moon-eye winking red and yellow through the
    dark.
Oh, the moon above the mountains red and yellow through the
    dark!

Across the seas of Wonderland to London-town we blundered,
Forty singing seamen as was puzzled for to know
If the visions that we saw was caused by—here again we pondered—
A tipple in a vision forty thousand years ago.
    Could the grog we *dreamt* we swallowed
    Make us *dream* of all that followed?
We were simply singing seamen, so of course we didn't know!
We were simply singing seamen, so of course we could not know!

337

THE ADMIRAL'S GHOST*

Alfred Noyes

I tell you a tale tonight
   Which a seaman told to me,
With eyes that gleamed in the lanthorn light
   And a voice as low as the sea.

You could almost hear the stars
   Twinkling up in the sky,
And the old wind woke and moaned in the spars,
   And the same old waves went by,

Singing the same old song
   As ages and ages ago,
While he froze my blood in that deep-sea night
   With the things that he seemed to know.

A bare foot pattered on deck;
   Ropes creaked; then—all grew still,
And he pointed his finger straight in my face
   And growled, as a sea dog will.

*Reprinted by permission of the publishers, J. B. Lippincott Company, from *Collected Poems in One Volume*, by Alfred Noyes. Copyright, 1906, 1922, 1947, by Alfred Noyes.

"Do 'ee know who Nelson was?
    That pore little shrivelled form
With the patch on his eye and the pinned-up sleeve
    And a soul like a North Sea storm?

"Ask of the Devonshire men!
    They know, and they'll tell you true;
He wasn't the pore little chawed-up chap
    That Hardy thought he knew.

"He wasn't the man you think!
    His patch was a dern disguise!
For he knew that they'd find him out, d'you see,
    If they looked him in both his eyes.

"He was twice as big as he seemed;
    But his clothes were cunningly made.
He'd both of his hairy arms all right!
    The sleeve was a trick of the trade.

"You've heard of sperrits, no doubt;
    Well, there's more in the matter than that!
But he wasn't the patch and he wasn't the sleeve,
    And he wasn't the laced cocked-hat.

"*Nelson was just—a Ghost!*
    You may laugh! But the Devonshire men
They knew that he'd come when England called,
    And they know that he'll come again.

"I'll tell you the way it was
    (For none of the landsmen know),
And to tell it you right, you must go a-starn
    Two hundred years or so.

"The waves were lapping and slapping
    The same as they are today;
And Drake lay dying aboard his ship
    In Nombre Dios Bay.

339

"The scent of the foreign flowers
  Came floating all around;
'But I'd give my soul for the smell o' the pitch,'
  Says he, 'in Plymouth sound.

" 'What shall I do,' he says,
  'When the guns begin to roar,
An' England wants me, and me not there
  To shatter 'er foes once more?'

"(You've heard what he said, maybe,
  But I'll mark you the p'ints again;
For I want you to box your compass right
  And get my story plain.)

" 'You must take my drum,' he says,
  'To the old sea-wall at home;
And if ever you strike that drum,' he says,
  'Why, strike me blind, I'll come!

" 'If England needs me, dead
  Or living, I'll rise that day!
I'll rise from the darkness under the sea
  Ten thousand miles away.'

"That's what he said; and he died;
  An' his pirates, listenin' roun'
With their crimson doublets and jewelled swords
  That flashed as the sun went down.

"They sewed him up in his shroud
  With a round-shot top and toe,
To sink him under the salt sharp sea
  Where all good seamen go.

"They lowered him down in the deep,
  And there in the sunset light
They boomed a broadside over his grave,
  As meanin' to say 'Good night.'

340

"They sailed away in the dark
   To the dear little isle they knew;
And they hung his drum by the old sea-wall
   The same as he told them to.

"Two hundred years went by,
   And the guns began to roar,
And England was fighting hard for her life,
   As ever she fought of yore.

" 'It's only my dead that count,'
   She said, as she says today;
'It isn't the ships and it isn't the guns
   'Ull sweep Trafalgar's Bay.'

"D'you guess who Nelson was?
   You may laugh, but it's true as true!
There was more in that pore little chawed-up chap
   Than ever his best friend knew.

"The foe was creepin' close,
   In the dark, to our white-cliffed isle;
They were ready to leap at England's throat,
   When—O, you may smile, you may smile;

"But— ask of the Devonshire men;
   For they heard in the dead of night
The roll of a drum, and they saw him pass
   On a ship all shining white.

"He stretched out his dead cold face
   And he sailed in the grand old way!
The fishes had taken an eye and his arm,
   But he swept Trafalgar's Bay.

"Nelson—was Francis Drake!
   O, what matters the uniform,
Or the patch on your eye or your pinned-up sleeve,
   If your soul's like a North Sea storm?"

Part XI: OUR WORLD

GOD'S WORLD*
Edna St. Vincent Millay

O world, I cannot hold thee close enough!
  Thy winds, thy wide gray skies!
  Thy mists, that roll and rise!
Thy woods, this autumn day, that ache and sag
And all but cry with color! That gaunt crag
To crush! To lift the lean of that black bluff!
World, world! I cannot get thee close enough!

Long have I known a glory in it all
  But never knew I this,
  Here such a passion is
As stretcheth me apart. Lord, I do fear
Thou'st made the world too beautiful this year.
My soul is all but out of me—let fall
No burning leaf; prithee, let no bird call.

THE LISTENERS

Walter de la Mare

"Is there anybody there?" said the Traveler,
  Knocking on the moonlit door;
And his horse in the silence champed the grasses
  Of the forest's ferny floor:
And a bird flew up out of the turret,
  Above the Traveler's head:
And he smote upon the door again a second time,
  "Is there anybody there?" he said.
But no one descended to the Traveler;
  No head from the leaf-fringed sill
Leaned over and looked into his gray eyes,
  Where he stood perplexed and still.
But only a host of phantom listeners
  That dwelt in the lone house then
Stood listening in the quiet of the moonlight
  To that voice from the world of men:
Stood thronging the faint moonbeams on the dark stair,
  That goes down to the empty hall,
Hearkening in an air stirred and shaken
  By the lonely Traveler's call.
And he felt in his heart their strangeness,
  Their stillness answering his cry,
While his horse moved, cropping the dark turf,
  'Neath the starred and leafy sky;
For he suddenly smote on the door, even
  Louder, and lifted his head:—
"Tell them I came, and no one answered,
  That I kept my word," he said.
Never the least stir made the listeners,
  Though every word he spake
Fell echoing through the shadowiness of the still house
  From the one man left awake:
Ay, they heard his foot upon the stirrup,
  And the sound of iron on stone
And how the silence surged softly backward
  When the plunging hoofs were gone.

THE WEST WIND
John Masefield

It's a warm wind, the west wind, full of birds' cries;
I never hear the west wind, but tears are in my eyes.
For it comes from the west lands, the old brown hills,
And April's in the west wind, and daffodils.

It's a fine land, the west land, for hearts as tired as mine;
Apple orchards blossom there, and the air's like wine.
There is cool green grass there, where men may lie at rest;
And the thrushes are in song there, fluting from the nest.

"Will you not come home, brother? You have been long away.
It's April, and blossomtime, and white is the spray:
And bright is the sun, brother, and warm is the rain;
Will you not come home, brother, home to us again?

"The young corn is green, brother, where the rabbits run;
It's blue sky, and white clouds, and warm rain and sun.
It's song to a man's soul, brother, fire to a man's brain,
To hear the wild bees and see the merry spring again.

"Larks are singing in the west, brother, above the green wheat,
So will you not come home, brother, and rest your tired feet?
I've a balm for bruised hearts, brother, sleep for aching eyes,"
Says the warm wind, the west wind, full of birds' cries.

It's the white road westwards is the road I must tread
To the green grass, the cool grass, and rest for heart and head,
To the violets and the brown brooks and the thrushes' song
In the fine land, the west land, the land where I belong.

ABRAHAM LINCOLN WALKS AT MIDNIGHT

Vachel Lindsay

It is portentous, and a thing of state
  That here at midnight, in our little town
A mourning figure walks, and will not rest
  Near the old courthouse pacing up and down.

Or by his homestead, or in shadowed yards
  He lingers where his children used to play,
Or through the market, on the well-worn stones
  He stalks until the dawn-stars burn away.

A bronzed, lank man! His suit of ancient black,
  A famous high-top-hat and plain worn shawl
Make him the quaint great figure that men love,
  The prairie-lawyer, master of us all.

He cannot sleep upon his hillside now.
  He is among us, as in times before!
And we who toss and lie awake for long
  Breathe deep, and start, to see him pass the door.

His head is bowed. He thinks on men and kings.
  Yea, when the sick world cries, how can he sleep?
Too many peasants fight, they know not why,
  Too many homesteads in black terror weep.

The sins of all the war lords burn his heart.
  He sees the dreadnaughts scouring every main.
He carries on his shawl-wrapt shoulders now
  The bitterness, the folly, and the pain.

He cannot rest until a spirit-dawn
  Shall come;—the shining hope of Europe free;
The league of sober folk, the Workers' Earth
  Bringing long peace to Cornland, Alp, and Sea.

It breaks his heart that kings must murder still,
  That all his hours of travail here for men
Seem yet in vain. And who will bring white peace
  That he may sleep upon his hill again?

A SONG OF SHERWOOD*

Alfred Noyes

Sherwood in the twilight, is Robin Hood awake?
Gray and ghostly shadows are gliding through the brake,
Shadows of the dappled deer, dreaming of the morn,
Dreaming of a shadowy man that winds a shadowy horn.

Robin Hood is here again: all his merry thieves
Hear a ghostly bugle-note shivering through the leaves,
Calling as he used to call, faint and far away,
In Sherwood, in Sherwood, about the break of day.

Merry, merry England has kissed the lips of June;
All the wings of fairyland were here beneath the moon,
Like a flight of rose-leaves fluttering in a mist
Of opal and ruby and pearl and amethyst.

Merry, merry England is waking as of old,
With eyes of blither hazel and hair of brighter gold;
For Robin Hood is here again beneath the bursting spray
In Sherwood, in Sherwood, about the break of day.

Love is in the greenwood building him a house
Of wild rose and hawthorn and honeysuckle boughs;
Love is in the greenwood, dawn is in the skies,
And Marian is waiting with a glory in her eyes.

Hark! The dazzled laverock climbs the golden steep!
Marian is waiting; is Robin Hood asleep?
Round the fairy grass-rings frolic elf and fay,
In Sherwood, in Sherwood, about the break of day.

*Reprinted by permission of the publishers, J. B. Lippincott Company, from *Collected Poems in One Volume*, by Alfred Noyes. Copyright, 1906, 1922, 1947, by Alfred Noyes.

Oberon, Oberon, rake away the gold,
Rake away the red leaves, roll away the mold,
Rake away the gold leaves, roll away the red,
And wake Will Scarlett from his leafy forest bed.

Friar Tuck and Little John are riding down together
With quarter-staff and drinking-can and gray goose-feather.
The dead are coming back again, the years are rolled away
In Sherwood, in Sherwood, about the break of day.

Softly over Sherwood the south wind blows.
All the heart of England hid in every rose
Hears across the greenwood the sunny whisper leap,
Sherwood in the red dawn, is Robin Hood asleep?

Hark, the voice of England wakes him as of old
And, shattering the silence with a cry of brighter gold,
Bugles in the greenwood echo from the steep,
Sherwood in the red dawn, is Robin Hood asleep?

Where the deer are gliding down the shadowy glen
All across the glades of fern he calls his merry men—
Doublets of the Lincoln green glancing through the May
In Sherwood, in Sherwood, about the break of day—

Calls them and they answer: from aisles of oak and ash
Rings the *Follow! Follow!* and the boughs begin to crash,
The ferns begin to flutter and the flowers begin to fly,
And through the crimson dawning the robber band goes by.

Robin! Robin! Robin! All his merry thieves
Answer as the bugle-note shivers through the leaves,
Calling as he used to call, faint and far away,
In Sherwood, in Sherwood, about the break of day.

STRANGE HOLINESS

Robert P. Tristram Coffin

There is a strange holiness around
Our common days on common ground.

I have heard it in the birds
Whose voices reach above all words,

Going upward, bars on bars,
Until they sound as high as stars.

I have seen it in the snake,
A flowing jewel in the brake.

It has sparkled in my eyes
In luminous breath of fireflies.

I have come upon its track
Where trilliums curled their petals back.

I have seen it flash in under
The towers of the midnight thunder.

Once, I met it face to face
In a fox pressed by the chase.

He came down the road on feet
Quiet and fragile, light as heat.

He had a fish still set and bright
In his slender jaws held tight.

His ears were conscious, whetted darts,
His eyes had small flames in their hearts.

The preciousness of life and breath
Glowed through him as he outran death.

Strangeness and secrecy and pride
Ran rippling down his golden hide.

His beauty was not meant for me,
With my dull eyes, so close to see.

Unconscious of me, rapt, alone,
He came, and then stopped still as stone.

His eyes went out as in a gust,
His beauty crumbled into dust.

There was but a ruin there,
A hunted creature, stripped and bare.

Then he faded at one stroke
Like a dingy, melting smoke.

But there his fish lay like a key
To the bright, lost mystery.

BARTER

Sara Teasdale

Life has loveliness to sell,
    All beautiful and splendid things,
Blue waves whitened on a cliff,
    Soaring fire that sways and sings,
And children's faces looking up,
Holding wonder like a cup.

Life has loveliness to sell,
    Music like a curve of gold,
Scent of pine trees in the rain,
    Eyes that love you, arms that hold,
And for your spirit's still delight,
Holy thoughts that star the night.

Spend all you have for loveliness,
    Buy it and never count the cost;
For one white singing hour of peace
    Count many a year of strife well lost,
And for a breath of ecstasy
Give all you have been, or could be.

351

HIGH FLIGHT

John Gillespie Magee, Jr.

Oh, I have slipped the surly bonds of earth,
And danced the skies on laughter-silvered wings;
Sunward I've climbed and joined the tumbling mirth
Of sun-split clouds—and done a hundred things
You have not dreamed of—wheeled and soared and swung
High in the sunlit silence. Hovering there,
I've chased the shouting wind along and flung
My eager craft through footless halls of air.
Up, up the long delirious, burning blue
I've topped the wind-swept heights with easy grace,
Where never lark, or even eagle, flew;
And, while with silent, lifting mind I've trod
The high untrespassed sanctity of space,
Put out my hand and touched the face of God.

HE WHOM A DREAM HATH POSSESSED

Shaemus O'Sheel

He whom a dream hath possessed knoweth no more of doubting,
For mist and the blowing of winds and the mouthing of words he
  scorns;
Not the sinuous speech of schools he hears, but a knightly shouting,
And never comes darkness down, yet he greeteth a million morns.
He whom a dream hath possessed knoweth no more of roaming;
All roads and the flowing of waves and the speediest flight he
  knows,
But wherever his feet are set, his soul is forever homing,
And going, he comes, and coming, he heareth a call and goes.
He whom a dream hath possessed knoweth no more of sorrow,
At death and the dropping of leaves and the fading of suns he
  smiles,
For a dream remembers no past and scorns the desire of a morrow,
And a dream in a sea of doom sets surely the ultimate isles.
He whom a dream hath possessed treads the impalpable marches,
From the dust of the day's long road he leaps to a laughing star,
And the ruin of worlds that fall he views from eternal arches,
And rides God's battlefield in a flashing and golden car.

352

COUNTRY CHURCH
Robert P. Tristram Coffin

He could not separate the thought
Of God from daisies white and hot
In blinding thousands by a road,
Or dandelion disks that glowed
Like little suns upon the ground.
Holiness was like the sound
Of thousands of tumultuous bees
In full-blossomed apple trees,
Or it was smell of standing grain,
Or robins singing up a rain.

For the church he went to when
He was eight and nine and ten,
And good friends with the trees and sun,
Was a small white country one.
The caraway's lace parasols
Brushed the clapboards of its walls,
The grass flowed round it east and west,
And one blind had a robin's nest.
Before the sermon was half over,
It turned to fragrance of red clover.

May and June and other weather
And farmers' wives came in together,
At every window swung a bough,
Always, far off, someone's cow
Lowed and lowed at every pause.
The rhythms of the mighty laws
That keep men going, to their graves,
Were no holier than the waves
The wind made in the tasselled grass
A small boy saw through window glass.

NIGHT

Sara Teasdale

Stars over snow.
    And in the west a planet
Swinging below a star—
    Look for a lovely thing and
        you will find it.
It is not far—
    It never will be far.

CANTICLE OF THE SUN

St. Francis of Assisi

TRANSLATION OF *Matthew Arnold*

O most high, almighty, good Lord God, to Thee belong praise,
    glory, honor, and all blessing!
Praised be my Lord God with all His creatures; and specially our
    brother the sun, who brings us the day, and who brings us the
    light; fair is he, and shining with a very great splendor; O Lord,
    he signifies to us Thee!
Praised be my Lord for our sister the moon, and for the stars, the
    which He has set clear and lovely in heaven.
Praised be my Lord for our brother the wind, and for air and
    cloud, calms and all weather, by the which Thou upholdest life
    in all creatures.
Praised be my Lord for our sister water, who is very serviceable
    unto us, and humble, and precious, and clean.
Praised be my Lord for our brother fire, through whom Thou
    givest us light in the darkness; and he is bright, and pleasant,
    and very mighty, and strong.
Praised be my Lord for our mother the earth, the which doth sus-
    tain us and keep us, and bringeth forth divers'fruits, and flowers
    of many colors and grass. . . .
Praise ye, and bless ye the Lord, and give thanks unto Him, and
    serve Him with great humility.

mister mckee

THE LAKE ISLE OF INNISFREE
William Butler Yeats

I will arise and go now, and go to Innisfree,
And a small cabin build there, of clay and
    wattles made;
Nine bean rows will I have there, a hive for
    the honey bee,
And live alone in the bee-loud glade.

And I shall have some peace there, for peace
    comes dropping slow,
Dropping from the veils of the morning to
    where the cricket sings;
There midnight's all a-glimmer, and noon
    a purple glow,
And evening full of the linnet's wings.

I will arise and go now, for always night
    and day
I hear lake water lapping with low sounds
    by the shore;
While I stand on the roadway, or on the
    pavements gray,
I hear it in the deep heart's core.

TREES

Joyce Kilmer

I think that I shall never see
A poem lovely as a tree.
A tree whose hungry mouth is prest
Against the earth's sweet flowing breast;
A tree that looks at God all day,
And lifts her leafy arms to pray;
A tree that may in summer wear
A nest of robins in her hair;
Upon whose bosom snow has lain;
Who intimately lives with rain.
Poems are made by fools like me,
But only God can make a tree.

LOVELIEST OF TREES

A. E. Housman

Loveliest of trees, the cherry now
Is hung with bloom along the bough,
And stands about the woodland ride
Wearing white for Eastertide.

Now, of my threescore years and ten,
Twenty will not come again,
And take from seventy springs a score,
It only leaves me fifty more.

And since to look at things in bloom
Fifty springs are little room,
About the woodlands I will go
To see the cherry hung with snow.

STOPPING BY WOODS ON A
SNOWY EVENING

Robert Frost

Whose woods these are I think I know.
His house is in the village though;
He will not see me stopping here
To watch his woods fill up with snow.

The little horse must think it queer
To stop without a farmhouse near
Between the woods and frozen lake
The darkest evening of the year.

He gives his harness bells a shake
To ask if there is some mistake.
The only other sound's the sweep
Of easy wind and downy flake.

The woods are lovely dark and deep.
But I have promises to keep,
And miles to go before I sleep,
And miles to go before I sleep.

TRAVEL*

Edna St. Vincent Millay

The railroad track is miles away,
    And the day is loud with voices speaking,
Yet there isn't a train goes by all day
    But I hear its whistle shrieking.

All night there isn't a train goes by,
    Though the night is still for sleep and dreaming,
But I see its cinders in the sky,
    And hear its engine steaming.

My heart is warm with the friends I make,
    And better friends I'll not be knowing,
Yet there isn't a train I wouldn't take,
    No matter where it's going.

*From *Second April*, published by Harper & Brothers. Copyright, 1921, 1949, by Edna St. Vincent Millay.

357

SEA–FEVER

John Masefield

I must go down to the seas again, to the
    lonely sea and the sky,
And all I ask is a tall ship and a star to steer
    her by,
And the wheel's kick and the wind's song
    and the white sail's shaking,
And a gray mist on the sea's face and a gray
    dawn breaking.

I must go down to the seas again, for the
    call of the running tide
Is a wild call and a clear call that may not
    be denied;
And all I ask is a windy day with the white
    clouds flying,
And the flung spray and the blown spume,
    and the sea-gulls crying.

I must go down to the seas again to the
    vagrant gypsy life,
To the gull's way and the whale's way where
    the wind's like a whetted knife;
And all I ask is a merry yarn from a laughing
    fellow-rover,
And quiet sleep and a sweet dream when
    the long trick's over.

Index